# ANIMAL
## TALES

**JAY HEALE**

# AFRICAN
# ANIMAL
# TALES

Struik Lifestyle
(an imprint of Random House Struik (Pty) Ltd)
Company Reg. No. 1966/003153/07
80 McKenzie Street, Cape Town 8001
PO Box 1144, Cape Town, 8000, South Africa

First published as *South African Animal Adventures* by
Struik Timmins Publishers in 1991, and *True African Animal Tales* by
Struik Publishers (Pty) Ltd in 1995
This combined edition published in 2001 by Struik Publishers
Reprinted 2003, 2004, 2006, 2008
Reprinted by Struik Lifestyle in 2009

ISBN 978-1-86872-704-9

**Publisher:** Linda de Villiers
**Managing editor:** Cecilia Barfield
**Cover designer:** Bev Dodd
**Border design on cover:** Sharon Bernhardt
**Illustrators:** Gina Daniel, Lorreta Chegwidden and Graeme Chegwidden
**Page designers:** Darren McLean, Robert Meas
**Reproduction:** Hirt & Carter Cape (Pty) Ltd, Unifoto (Pty) Ltd
**Printing and binding:** Times Offset (M) Sdn Bhd

# Contents

# Introduction

'It must all be true! Don't leave out anything!' That was how the children around Sir Percy FitzPatrick urged him to tell the tale of our famous Jock of the Bushveld. Although Jock was one of our first true animal heroes, there are many other stories worth knowing. From years past come such animal characters as Huberta the hippo and Just Nuisance of Simonstown. From more recent years the Magnificent Seven elephants of the Kruger Park and the mare Beauty, the first horse in South Africa to receive a medal for bravery.

Here are snippets of history viewed through Somerset, the famous horse of Dick King, and the once common mass migration of game. Alongside these are stories that represent the work of caring organisations such as SANCCOB and the SPCA and the Police Dog Unit. They are all true stories.

We live in a world that often forgets the need for 'balance'. So you will read here both of human beings assisting animals and of heroes of the animal world who have helped us.

I am delighted that Struik Publishers have put these two collections of animal stories into one book and once again made them available. My repeated thanks to all those who helped me with the original field research. To you, the reader, Happy Reading!

**JAY HEALE**

**2001**

# JUST NUISANCE

Many naval ships have had animal mascots – and many army regiments as well – but none have gained the same fame and popular affection as the Great Dane which was enlisted as a member of the Royal Navy just before the outbreak of the Second World War.

The puppy, bought by Benjamin Chaney in March 1938, was hardly a year old and it was already clear that he was going to grow into a large dog. When Benjamin and his wife were put in charge of the United Services Institute at Simon's Town, they took the young dog along. Most of their customers were naval ratings, wearing bell-bottomed dark blue trousers, the well-known three-striped collar and flat-topped seaman's cap. These were the humans who became the Great Dane's friends. Officers he tolerated and women he ignored!

It was just as well for the Chaneys' food bill that their dog enjoyed the company of the navy. A whole can of corned beef was merely a snack for him! Before long, at least one naval steward was craftily filling out his monthly return to include large amounts of canned corned beef which, when opened, "proved to have meat unfit for human consumption". These had been disposed of – in Nuisance's direction!

This name was swiftly awarded when the crew of HMS *Neptune* found they had to step around the huge dog's body as he sunned himself on one of their gangways. "You ... nuisance!" they complained – and the name stuck.

Simon's Town offered very little in the way of entertainment, so when the naval ratings were granted leave, they would board the train to Cape Town. Nuisance decided to go with his friends, but without a ticket. If a brave ticket-collector managed to persuade Nuisance to leave, he would either climb aboard again through the nearest open window or sit down on the platform and wait for the next train. The South African Railways authorities became increasingly annoyed and eventually threatened Chaney that the dog would be destroyed if it continued travelling without a ticket.

Messages were rushed around Simon's Town. How dare anyone threaten their huge pet? The Commander-in-Chief South Atlantic found himself swamped with letters of protest. So the decision was made. The dog Nuisance was to be officially enlisted as a member of the Royal Navy. That way the Admiralty could issue him with a season ticket.

On 25 August 1939, Nuisance entered the recruiting office of HMS *Afrikander I* for his papers to be registered. His trade was described as 'Bonecrusher' and his religion as 'Scrounger'. No one knew what to put as his Christian name until someone suggested,

"Leave it out and give the name as just Nuisance." So the brainwave was accepted! And Able Seaman Just Nuisance was enroled in King George VI's Royal Navy. His name, rank and official number were fastened to his collar.

Just Nuisance was also supplied with a regulation seaman's cap. The strap under his chin annoyed him. He even gave a sigh when it was taken off at night. In due course he was given official authority to be the only member of the Royal Navy to be excused from wearing a seaman's cap.

He was billeted in Hut Number One where he had a bed of his own, took his meals at the same time as the other ratings, and was given shore leave every night. Corned beef and lamb chops were his favourite foods, followed by milk chocolate and ice cream. To drink he liked lager beer. Buying Nuisance a drink became so popular that a special notice had to be posted requesting all canteens and bars in Simon's Town not to serve him more than his nightly ration of six quarts (about 14 cans).

Though Just Nuisance had no official duties, he still contributed vigorously to South Africa's war effort by attending charity gatherings to raise money. In August 1941, he was 'married' to a Great Dane bitch named Adinda. When the resulting two puppies were old enough, they and Just Nuisance were welcomed to Cape Town by the Mayor and Mayoress and cheering crowds. The pups were full of bounce, tails wagging, tongues hanging out. Just Nuisance sniffed at them and gave one growl which seemed to mean, "If you're my kids, then behave yourselves." They did! And the puppies were sold by auction to raise funds for the war. So, even Just Nuisance contributed to the war effort.

The GREAT DANE is a massive and powerful dog, with a muscular, well-formed body and a long arched neck. Its coat is very short and smooth, and is usually gold or black, or even a combination of the two colours. Originally bred in Germany to hunt wild boar, the Great Dane, despite its size and appearance, is generally friendly and playful, but is a very good watchdog and only aggressive when it is threatened.

Many letters arrived requesting the presence of the popular Great Dane at local fêtes and functions. In that way, he helped to raise hundreds of pounds for war funds. However, he simply couldn't go everywhere he was invited. Letters were written in reply on his behalf. He turned down one invitation on the grounds that "My C.O. informs me that my appearance might result in a flood of applications for service with the Royal Navy". To another admirer who seemed to think he was a sheepdog, Just Nuisance replied, "I'm not a sheepdog, nor do I like sheep except as mutton."

Life at Simon's Town wasn't all hard work. One day, Just Nuisance was sun-bathing beside the open-air pool. A fat officer dived in with a whale-like splash, swam a length (with much puffing and panting) and hauled himself out. The Great Dane was lying slightly in his way, so the nasty officer put a foot under the dog's belly and tipped him into the pool.

Just Nuisance swam up to the surface and looked hard at the officer, who was laughing loudly. Then he swam to the side where two of his friends helped him out. He shook himself dry and watched as the officer, still chuckling, dived in again. When he climbed out, Just Nuisance was waiting.

The Great Dane leapt forward and thrust his fore paws into the fat officer's bulging belly. As the man toppled helplessly back into the water, Just Nuisance gave one ear-shattering bark of triumph.

Amid the howls of laughter from all the sailors around, the officer threatened serious punishments for all of them and particularly for Able Seaman Just Nuisance. But nothing further happened.

One officer's indignation was unimportant compared to the way he befriended the hundreds

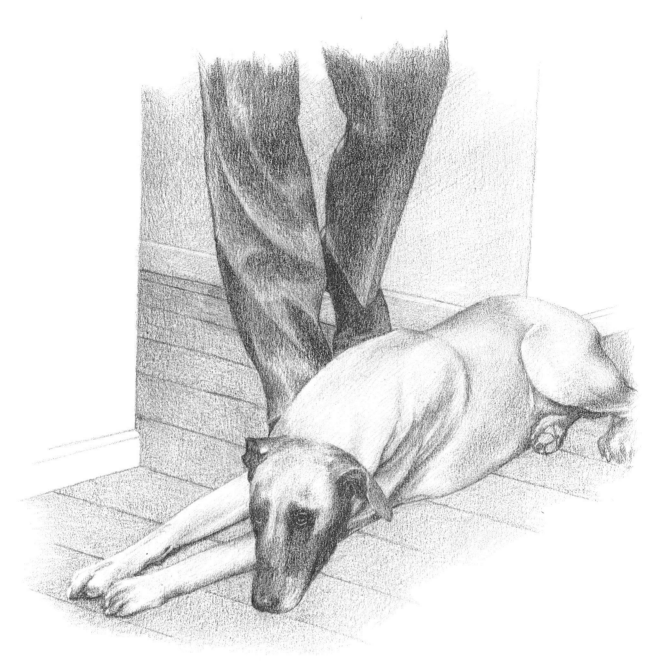

of ordinary seamen who visited Simon's Town. Just Nuisance knew nothing of the war these men were fighting. He knew only that they were honest workers who deserved his friendship.

Towards the end of 1943, it became clear that Just Nuisance was not well. He enjoyed riding in the naval transport lorries and often jumped off if he saw some of his friends walking past, and never bothered about how fast the lorry was moving. This had damaged his legs and now he was crippled with pain. For a few days he was given treatment at the naval hospital, where he lay stretched out sideways on a bed – with a bottle of lager beer as medicine on the bedside cupboard! He appeared to improve and was discharged as "fit for duty".

A month later he was very ill. A kind vet offered to look after him at his own home, but it soon became clear that Just Nuisance was in constant pain and that there was no chance of his recovery. Sorrowfully, the decision was taken that he should be put quietly to sleep. This was done on 1 April 1944 – his seventh birthday.

All available officers and men attended the funeral, and there were few dry eyes among them. Wrapped in the White Ensign, the body of Just Nuisance was buried with full naval honours. A party of Royal Marines fired the last volleys over the grave.

# THE FRIENDLY LEOPARD

He lay in the bushes and watched the fishermen. He had seen them often before. These human beings didn't appear to be dangerous, though sometimes they made loud noises and played with fire. Since he left his mother to hunt on his own, the young leopard had kept out of sight of human beings. But now they were between him and the river. It had been a hot day and he was thirsty.

The leopard decided to go past them and down to the river. So he padded out from his hiding place, his paws making no sound on the dirt road.

But soon there was plenty of noise! Shrieks and yells, and running feet and car doors slamming, and engines starting up and bakkies driving away. People fell over each other and piled into the cars, whether the cars belonged to them or not!

That was a Saturday in mid-December, 1986 – and the story of the Betty's Bay leopard had begun.

About a week after the fishermen had encountered the leopard on the beach, the leopard padded its way into a braai area nearby. Again, there was a moment of panic as the humans rushed into the sea for safety. But then one girl darted back to fetch her camera and the leopard didn't seem to mind at all. She walked to within ten metres of the animal and took several photographs, while he sat there like a tame fireside cat. Already, his reputation as 'the friendly leopard' was growing.

But there was nothing friendly about the leopard when he discovered a breeding colony of jackass penguins in the reserve at Stony Point. Leopards kill to eat, by instinct. They often store the carcass of a large animal in a tree and return to it as a 'food store'. Perhaps sensing that one penguin was not a full meal, the leopard attacked the defenceless, waddling birds and in two nights he killed about 50

of them. From his point of view, the penguins were an easy source of food, but local opinion about the leopard suddenly changed from an amusing curiosity to a threatening and dangerous killer.

Concerned residents of Betty's Bay contacted biologist Peter Norton of the Cape Department of Nature and Environmental Conservation. He had made a special study of leopards in the Cape, so he went to investigate.

Concerned people had started to gather the pathetic bodies of the penguins. On the dead birds were tooth marks – certainly those of some large predator, either a lynx or leopard. And there was plenty of leopard spoor on the sandy patches around the reserve.

On a path were several tracks showing that the leopard came that way often, and Peter and his helpers started positioning a trap. It was a heavy cage with a steel frame and wire mesh. Hauling it into position was a rowdy affair. Suddenly one of the men pointed to behind Peter's back. Curious at the noise, the leopard had come to investigate. It was sitting watching them.

In the glowing light of the setting sun, the leopard looked even more golden. Peter Norton was very excited and quickly fetched his equipment from the bakkie. He couldn't waste the opportunity to shoot the leopard several times – with his camera. Lying relaxed on a rock, it gazed at him without seeming to be disturbed at all.

They set the trap and baited it with one of the dead penguins. As they retreated, the leopard strolled forward and sniffed at the cage. Cautiously, he pushed his head inside, seized the penguin and slid out without setting off the trap.

Peter then put another dead bird in the trap and, without hesitation, the leopard returned for a second helping. But this time he was too confident and the door snapped shut with a thud. He was caught.

After the widely reported killing of the penguins, such a swift capture of the 'murderer' made an excellent story for the newspapers and television. When Peter and his team returned to Stony Point the next morning, there were plenty of spectators, reporters and cameramen.

The Betty's Bay leopard was fast becoming famous.

The leopard lay relaxed in its cage, only objecting with a slight snarl when Peter approached and aimed his blowpipe. He blew the tranquillising dart into its rump. After some minutes, the leopard slumped as the powerful drug took effect.

The cage was opened and the beautiful spotted cat taken out. Working swiftly, Peter weighed and measured the animal. It was a male, about one to two years old, not yet grown to full size. Not much bigger than Peter's own golden retriever dog – but a lot more powerful. Around the leopard's neck he fastened a tough green collar with a radio device which would enable them to trace the leopard's movements.

"Where are you taking him?" asked one of the curious spectators.

"I can't tell you exactly," said Peter. "But it's somewhere out of harm's way in the mountains."

"He's beautiful!" murmured a boy, stroking the unconscious leopard.

"Nasty, dangerous thing," grumbled an adult nearby. "I'm glad to see the last of him."

The cage was placed in some high grass near a mountain stream in the heart of the Kogelberg Reserve. The door was opened and the leopard, sniffing the air, slid out to freedom.

The LEOPARD has a heavier head than the cheetah, and has rosettes of dark markings rather than spots like the cheetah. The leopard also has no dark 'tear lines' on its face. Normally, leopards hunt alone and at night and seldom allow themselves to be seen by man.

Leopards eat a wide variety of prey: mice, small antelope, birds and even river fish. A leopard does not roar like a lion: it gives a rasping cough or a growl.

Peter scratched his beard and wished the leopard good luck. But the leopard had other ideas.

In the warmth of a festive Saturday evening, just after Christmas, a young lady jumped into her car and, for a short distance, her fluffy miniature poodle ran playfully along behind.

Suddenly, out of the bushes appeared a slim yellow shape, speckled with black. The dog gave one frantic bark before the powerful jaws seized it and the leopard disappeared into the undergrowth. The news spread through the little town at once.

"The leopard is back!"

But there was no evidence that it was the Betty's Bay leopard. Peter Norton was fairly certain that it was *not*. Using the radio-collar, he had traced the leopard's movements for several days and 'his' leopard had been heading straight back towards the coastal region where he had been captured. That was expected, and Peter deliberately kept the press informed. The more the public knew about the habits and behaviour of leopards, the better. Following the radio signals from an aeroplane, Peter discovered that the leopard was now in the Botanical Gardens at Betty's Bay. By the time he had landed the plane and driven to the Gardens, he was met by three very disturbed gardeners. The leopard certainly *was* there!

"It jumped out of the bushes right in front of us. Made our hair stand on end! Then it bounded away into the garden."

So, while a television cameraman filmed the action from a cautious distance, Peter searched the bushes. Just before dark he managed to lure the leopard into the open to have his photograph taken again, before he slipped away.

Opinions of the residents were divided.

"It's a dangerous wild animal, I'm telling you, man."

"Nonsense! It's tame. It's our friendly leopard. It sat and looked at me like a puppy dog."

"If you leave it alone, it won't harm anybody."

Stories of hunters following wounded leopards have given them the reputation of savage behaviour, but this one was different. Most leopards living near civilisation hunt only at night because they are scared of humans. This one was unafraid of humans and seemed almost intrigued by them.

The next day Peter once again went in search of the leopard. He knew that if he could get the leopard and the photographer together, he had a unique opportunity to prove to television-watchers that wild animals did not need to be shot on sight.

Peter explained. "All wild animals *can* be unpredictable, but very few are naturally aggressive. You respect wild animals and they'll respect you. The very worst thing to do is to start screaming!"

So, while the fascinated cameraman followed and filmed every move, Peter and the leopard played 'cat and mouse' with each other. The leopard would hide and Peter would creep up close; then Peter would walk away and the leopard would trail him; then Peter hid and the leopard set out to find him. Not wishing to give the leopard a fright, Peter rose slowly from behind his bush. For a moment the two faces gazed at each other, one whiskered and one bearded, until the leopard strolled away. This leopard certainly was friendly.

Peter Norton knew that, for the leopard's own safety, he would have to be moved to a reserve such as the one at Cape Point from which he could not escape. It would be only a matter of days before the leopard could be moved to safety.

But then Peter received a phone call from a farmer in Pringle Bay. He had seen a leopard near his grazing sheep. Peter drove out to the farmer's smallholding, but it was already too late. In the back of the farm bakkie lay the body of the leopard. The once glowing yellow eyes were now dull, and green flies were buzzing around them.

The bullet that killed this beautiful animal was just one more shot fired in the battle between farmers and wildlife. In its short life, this leopard had captured the public's attention and so made its own tremendous contribution to their awareness of the problem. There *are* still wild animals in Africa. It is the humans who need to live and let live.

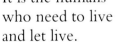

# Hatsi the Dassie

It was Christmas and the house was decorated with paper chains, strings of tinsel and a real Christmas tree with balls and baubles and chocolate bells wrapped in silver foil. At least that is what it looked like at night, when Susan and Steven went to bed.

In the morning, all the decorations were tattered and chewed, several chocolate bells were missing, and the presents under the tree showed clear teeth marks. Christmas was certainly not the right time of year to welcome a mischievous, little orphan dassie into the house!

"It's fun," said Susan, trying to convince herself.
"It's monstrous," said Steven and he meant it.

What was more, there were two of them. Two sweet, furry, young dassies, each about the size of a rat with no tail. They had fat cheeks, black button noses and nibbled with two flat, plastic-looking teeth on the top and a row of tiny teeth on the bottom. Both had pale eyebrows and their mouths had a permanent silly grin.

"They're so soft and friendly," said Susan protectively, as she stroked the soft brown hair on their round little tummies.

"Then why do they try to bite me?" asked Steven. "I only tried to stroke one, and he whirled around and threatened me!"

"That's because of their 'touch hairs'," explained Susan. "The hairs tell the dassie how close it is to things. Like an early-warning system."

Steven wasn't impressed.

All the books Susan had studied insisted that dassies are very lazy and do nothing for most of the day. Her two weren't like that at all. Like most small children, they were on the move all the time. They thought that good, healthy food was boring. They preferred to have a leisurely chew on more interesting items – preferably elastic or plastic or cotton wool.

They could climb just about anything. The pads on their feet actually sweat, which gives them enough grip to climb almost straight up steep cliffs. Their greatest game, apart from climbing the walls, was to jump on top of the kitchen dustbin which had a flip top. So they fell in. Then they squealed until Susan came to rescue them and put them on the floor, from where they could both jump back up again.

Susan and Steven did not agree about having dassies in the house, and they certainly could not agree on any names. 'Hansel and Gretel' was turned down flat – these were no fairy-tale characters! Susan wondered romantically about 'Romeo and Juliet'. Steven suggested 'Chew and Chomp' as being far more suitable. For the time being the two dassies had to be satisfied with plain 'He and She'.

But there weren't going to be two for much longer. She fell ill. She had an upset tummy and none of the cures that Susan tried had any effect. The vet felt her carefully and admitted that though dassies were not his usual patients, her insides didn't feel normal.

"Is it possible," asked the vet, "that she has eaten something harmful?"

Steven snorted. "Is there anything she hasn't eaten?"

"Then perhaps I'd better open her up and have a look. Bring her to my surgery tomorrow."

Susan stayed up all night with the suffering dassie, trying to encourage her to eat something. She needed food inside her for strength, as she hadn't eaten all day. She did nibble a little fish, which she had never touched before. Susan managed to get her to drink some medicine for her aching tummy. She chirruped with pleasure at the taste, and He promptly arrived to try some. Susan had to stop them arguing over it.

Poor She! Her tummy was so sore that she whistled faintly all the time. She didn't know whether to sit or stand or lie on the heating pad which Susan had provided as a bed. By morning, She seemed to have gained a little strength, but Susan was worried that it might not be enough.

The vet operated, but found nothing dangerous in her stomach, although he did notice that the stomach wall was thickened in some places and thin in others. But the shock of it all must have been too much for the little dassie, and She did not come round from the anaesthetic.

Left on his own, He was very sad and terribly alone. Steven tried to play with him, but the little dassie was not in a playful mood. He moped and whimpered, looking around nervously for his lost companion. Susan fetched her own precious teddy bear and

17

He snuggled up to it that night.

"Perhaps we're wrong to keep him," suggested Steven.

"Nonsense," said Susan. "He's unhappy. Wouldn't you be if I died? He needs company."

After a day of moping and another night with the teddy bear, the dassie suddenly cheered up and landed on the bed first thing in the morning. Having climbed all over Susan and Steven, he moved on to the bedside table and finished off the remains of last night's coffee from the bottom of the mugs.

"He likes mine better than yours," joked Steven.

"That's because you fill it with sugar," Susan decided. "He mustn't have too much. It'll be bad for his teeth."

"Hatsi Dassie!" said Steven, for no particular reason.

"Hatsi and teddy bear!"

"Hatsi-bear."

So that became He's new name. Hatsi decided that Susan was his new companion. He followed her everywhere. When Susan lay on her stomach on the floor – which was the position she liked best for reading – Hatsi would come running. He would first sniff her left ear to make sure it was the one he wanted, and then suck her earring with a soft but high-pitched squeal. Though Susan was expecting it, the noise always made her jump. When Hatsi had finished with her ear, he would gaze into space with his tongue out, sucking thoughtfully.

One day, the sitting room had been decorated for a children's party and there were balloons. Hatsi discovered that by standing on the back of the rocking-chair he could just reach one bunch. He stretched out and pulled. The bunch floated to the floor and Hatsi jumped off the chair quickly.

He sat beside the balloons and touched the first one carefully with his paws, feeling its shiny softness. It was twice his size. Then he discovered the knot and thoughtfully started to chew it. There was a loud pop (which must have been even louder for dassie ears) but Hatsi didn't flinch. He hesitated for a few seconds, obviously wondering if all balloons behaved like that, before he started on the next one. By the time Steven, shaking with laughter, had fetched Susan, the floor was covered with shreds of coloured rubber. Susan dashed to gather up the pieces.

"Hatsi might swallow some," she gasped.

"He probably has," was Steven's comment. "He's a plucky little fellow. I'm getting quite fond of him."

Hatsi chewed almost anything, but there was no doubt about what he wanted to eat: cereal, with milk, in different flavours. Hatsi would stand upright on his back feet, squealing, to indicate which flavour he had decided on. Oh, this stupid human! Why couldn't she understand? Susan would try a little of each until she found out what he was asking for. All biscuits were popular, however, and she had to hide the packets.

The sun shone in the late summer. There was nothing Hatsi-bear liked better than sun-bathing. He lay on his tummy with all four legs stretched out, drinking in the warmth from the stone stoep and the sun above.

Steven was busy, one day, scooping leaves out of the swimming pool with a long-handled net. Hatsi opened his eyes, blinked and saw something that interested him at the far side of the pool. He didn't appear to notice the large stretch of water in between. In mid run, he was suddenly treading on air and then splashed into the water. Steven forgot all about the net and jumped in, fully clothed. As he floated towards the surface, he could see the dassie above him, with all four feet paddling fiercely in the water.

"So dassies can swim," he observed, when he had hauled himself out and stood dripping by the pool with Hatsi unperturbed beside him. "There's more to this animal than I'd realised."

Though Steven was coming to like the furry, naughty Hatsi-bear dassie, Susan was growing desperate. She believed in discipline. Hatsi, however, had ideas of his own – and he loved Susan's sewing table with its treasure store of cotton reels, ribbons and bits of material.

"Off, off, off!" shouted Susan for the hundredth time as Hatsi jumped up.

The dassie scurried for cover behind a cushion until he thought Susan wasn't looking, and then jumped back again.

Susan sighed in loving despair, yet she was the one to object when Steven suggested that they take Hatsi with them on their coming holiday. A week at the coast, fishing and relaxing!

The DASSIE or rock rabbit could well be the 'hyrax' mentioned in the Bible. Living in colonies amongst the rocks, the dassie is a sun-lover; he only emerges when the sun is up, enjoys sun-bathing, and goes to sleep before sunset. You can find dassies all over South Africa, but you should approach them carefully. A watchful male will bark to warn the others. They can also grunt, growl, wail, twitter and snort.

"We'll never relax with Hatsi there," she moaned.

"But we can't leave him behind," Steven pointed out. "None of our friends are crazy enough to want him. Anyway, I rather enjoy the little chap's company. Let's give him a holiday as well."

So Hatsi-bear found himself in a holiday cottage by the sea. His first discovery was that the back of the fridge was wonderfully warm, and far easier to get into than the one at home. He curled up and went to sleep, while Steven and Susan searched desperately for him.

Then he discovered the world outside! He hopped on to the windowsill and couldn't believe his eyes. All he could see was trees and sea and space – an open horizon stretching away for ever. Hatsi sat and gazed and looked and dreamed and dozed on that windowsill all day long.

He didn't want to go out and join the world he could see. In fact, when Susan took him outside, he ran back in again and returned to his perch on the windowsill. There was so much out there which needed considering.

When he wasn't gazing out of the window, or guzzling down milk and cereal, he was sitting quietly on the arm of Susan's chair, with a piece of cobweb on the end of his nose. He was facing Susan, but she knew from the glazed look in his eyes and the blank expression on his little face that he was almost asleep. The wide world outside had given him far too much to think about.

So together they sat and dreamed of more holidays by the sea.

# Haig and Dimple

There have been several Haigs and Dimples in the Port Elizabeth Oceanarium, but the original dolphins deserve their fame.

Let's go back to a morning in October 1962. A friendly traffic officer brought the news that dolphins had been sighted off Summerstrand beach. Swiftly, Colin and Muriel and the rest of the team from the Oceanarium were on their way in a Landrover with a boat on a trailer behind. As they went charging down the beach, the traffic officer joined them.

"I phoned my boss and asked for a day off!" he explained.

The outboard motor was started and the boat pulled away, trailing a long spread of netting. They circled the school of dolphins, but several made a break for it and avoided the net. The boat turned in towards the shore, pulling the net closer around two dolphins in shallower water. The dolphins seemed quite calm, while the 300 people gathering on the beach were in a frenzy of excitement! Colin and Muriel rushed into the water and eased the dolphins ashore as they tried to escape the net. It was important not to let their skins become dry, so the onlookers were urged to keep splashing water on the dolphins.

One at a time, the dolphins were lifted on to the Landrover – a process that needed at least a dozen strong men. Swathed in spare items of clothing, the first dolphin was quickly driven to the Oceanarium. More willing hands were waiting there to help carry the heavy dolphin to her new home in the large dolphin pool.

While the vehicle raced back to fetch the second dolphin, they watched their first guest, apparently quite at ease as she swam lazily amongst the other 2 500 fish in the main tank.

The second dolphin arrived, helped in by the off-duty traffic officer. It was only seven minutes since they had caught the pair on the beach. The team stood at the observation window of the tank and heard a noise like birds chirping. The dolphins were talking to each other!

As they watched, the smaller dolphin came close up underneath the larger one, nuzzled her snout in and began to suckle her mother's teats. So the dolphins were mother and daughter!

Now all they needed were names. They were bottlenose dolphins and, as someone seemed sure those must be whisky bottles, the two were duly named Haig and Dimple, after a very famous brand of whisky.

Then came the training. Muriel was soon balanced on a ladder, dangling a fish. Her eyes were on Dimple, as Haig (the younger one) seemed too shy. Suddenly, pain flashed through her arm – as if a donkey was trying to swing from her finger! The fish had been snatched by Haig, who had also bitten

Muriel's index finger down to the bone. Muriel yelled in pain and scolded the young dolphin – and within a few days both Haig and Dimple were taking fish from her hands without snatching.

Gradually the dolphins gained confidence and stayed closer to their human friends. When a fish was fixed on the end of a bamboo stick, Haig was quite used to jumping for her titbit.

"Local dolphin leaps to fame" said the local paper, and crowds started arriving for a 'show'. Large coloured beach balls were left in Haig's pool so she could play. She was becoming quite tame, and Muriel had sessions of 'talking' to her. Haig would turn over in the water for her tummy to be rubbed, often finishing by closing her eyes and sinking to the bottom in sheer ecstasy.

But nothing would persuade Dimple to jump.

Dimple also refused to eat. She stayed out in the middle of the tank, swimming slowly with eyes half-closed, sometimes with Haig supporting her. One morning she was found dead in her tank. An examination showed that she was just a very old dolphin. There was no sign of disease or injury, and her teeth were well worn down. She had died of old age.

However, it seemed wise to find a new companion for Haig. So, about a month after Dimple's death, the news that three Indian dolphins had been caught, was received with much jubilation. When they were all placed in the same tank, they swam happily together, and Haig even tried to flirt with one of them. But though the Indian dolphins leapt out of the water occasionally, they would not jump for fish the way that Haig did.

"Why does Haig have to jump for her food?" a visitor asked one day. "Isn't that rather cruel?"

"The dolphins are fed regularly," Muriel explained. "The jumps are just part of the show, for an extra snack! And it certainly isn't cruel. The louder you clap, the higher Haig jumps! She loves showing off".

It was Colin who became Haig's main trainer. He taught her to play with a ball, to bring back rubber rings and to balance a plastic telephone on her nose. For extra style, she 'wore' a pair of outsize sunglasses. She even learned to jump through a hoop. Her act usually ended with the command from Colin, "Wave goodbye nicely!" whereupon she went underwater and stuck her tail out, waving a sort of goodbye.

He also made many recordings of the whistles and sounds made by her. Most dolphin sounds come from the blowhole at the top of the head through which they breathe, or through their vocal chords which produce notes much higher than humans can make. Their level of intelligence is similar to that of a six-year-old child. Haig was certainly more intelligent than some humans. One of her visitors said he had come to see the mermaid!

However, there was one trick which Colin could not train Haig to perform properly. He had a small organ built with five keys, trying to train Haig to press the right notes with her snout to play a tune. But Haig preferred to play her own tune! She could also blow a hooter bulb and ring a bell.

Between performances, Haig would swim around watching the audience, first with one eye, then the other. Perhaps she thought they were let in to entertain her!

By the time Haig had been at the Oceanarium for a year, the Indian dolphins had died. Another Dimple had been found but she had died too. Haig's next companion was a dolphin called Lady. Though Haig accepted Lady, she occasionally pined for other company. Her health was not helped by the litter discarded into the main pool. Once, Haig was so ill that she brought up two handkerchiefs, six sucker sticks, a baby's dummy, a plastic bag, a headscarf and a piece of bamboo.

When John Haig and Company, the whisky producers, donated a large sum of money to help build a larger pool, it seemed only fair that Lady should be renamed Lady Dimple!

But both dolphins were soon pining for company, and became uninterested in food. They swam slowly, refusing to perform any tricks or leaps. The situation was desperate. Telephone calls were made to America to have a male dolphin flown over, but there were none to spare.

Thanks to the friendly whisky distillers, the Oceanarium was given a new and larger net. With this, in due course, two male dolphins were caught on the same day. As the first newcomer was being pushed gently into the tank, Haig spotted it and almost went mad. She swam around the tank like a ship's torpedo. When the second bull dolphin

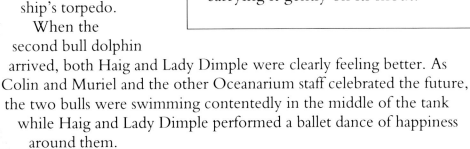

The DOLPHINS which perform at the Port Elizabeth Oceanarium are bottlenose dolphins. Up to 4 metres long, they are black or dark grey with a white belly. Any dolphin you see close inshore in South African waters is likely to be of this type, or perhaps an Indian dolphin which is grey, with a curved dorsal fin.

Dolphins are extremely intelligent creatures. Their friendliness towards humans is proven by the news report that, after the floods in Bangladesh following a cyclone, a dolphin brought a human baby to the shore, carrying it gently on its snout.

arrived, both Haig and Lady Dimple were clearly feeling better. As Colin and Muriel and the other Oceanarium staff celebrated the future, the two bulls were swimming contentedly in the middle of the tank while Haig and Lady Dimple performed a ballet dance of happiness around them.

Before long, Lady Dimple was seen to be pregnant. Telegrams of congratulation poured in from all over the country, and someone even put notices in the 'engagements' column of the Port Elizabeth newspaper.

And on that cheerful note, let us leave the happy dolphins!

# ADAM THE ELEPHANT

There actually are elephants in the Knysna forests. You won't see them very often, because they are wise enough to keep away from the traffic on the national road. But just occasionally, in the very early morning, one elephant may stroll across the road.

Back in June 1970, the game warden who was studying and listing the Knysna elephants, woke to the sound of hammering on his caravan. No, it wasn't an elephant! It was one of his helpers, and he was very excited.

"Listen! There's an elephant in the Garden of Eden."

It sounded suitable. There probably were elephants in that biblical Garden. The warden dressed hurriedly, grabbed his camera, and the two of them drove through the grey of dawn towards the popular picnic spot on the N2 freeway. The occasional car whizzed past, ignoring the ancient forest on either side and what creatures might live there. They saw nothing.

Suddenly, there he was. He stood in the dark among the trees, like a statue. The warden watched the elephant with pleasure. Appearing in the Garden of Eden, he just had to be called Adam! He was exactly right in that forest setting. It was the cars and humans and noise and litter that were out of place.

The warden looked hopefully through the view-finder of his camera. There wasn't enough light yet for a photograph. Still, he had to try. Quietly, he walked down the road, leaving his helper with instructions to stop any traffic if he could. The elephant was in full view now, facing the road with the ferns and shrubs up to his belly. Both big tusks were plainly visible, the left one slightly curved.

Then Adam saw the approaching human. The trunk went up and an ominous rumble came from it as he blew what was clearly a warning.

At that moment, there was a lull in the traffic and absolute silence reigned. The elephant returned to what was obviously on his mind. Without hesitation, he moved forward and stepped swiftly across the road. He seemed aware of the traffic, and had waited for the right moment to cross. The warden lifted his camera as Adam approached the white line in the middle and snapped the trigger. Then the elephant disappeared among the green trees of the forest on the other side of the road.

With the help of skilled trackers, the warden searched later that morning, and found Adam deep in the heart of the forest. There was no point in disturbing him and he seemed contented on his own. There were other elephants in that area. Perhaps he was on his way to join them.

Three days later, the phone rang in the forester's office.

"A message from Knysna. The elephants have completely destroyed the new timberyard on the main road."

The game warden was soon in his car, wondering as he drove how the elephants had managed to 'destroy' the stores of indigenous timber and the expensive chain wire fence. Would some fool now go out after them with a rifle? He put his foot down and overtook lorries full of logs in the style of police cars in the best films.

The timberyard didn't seem destroyed at all when he arrived. The wooden buildings were intact; so were the piles of valuable timber. There was a gap in the fence nearest the forest, where the elephants had broken in. At the other end, apparently seeking the normal way out, the elephants had found the gates locked. So they had put their feet on the top bar and flattened both halves of the gate.

There was no indication why they had done this damage. An extra half minute's walk would have taken them around it. But elephants are stubborn about their right of way. One local farmer had a

rose garden near the forest, and the elephants frequently cut across one corner of it. They would carefully push down the fence, help themselves to a mouthful of rosebush or azalea, and go on their way.

There was little that the warden could do at the timberyard except make encouraging noises to the forester, and express confidence that "steps would be taken". (By whom, the warden had no idea!)

Having picked up Adam's spoor in the forest nearby, the warden took steps of a different kind. There might be the chance of a better photograph this time. The tracks led towards a shallow valley, with huge old oak trees, near the old road to Knysna. At one point, Adam had pulled a tree down and it landed halfway across the road. An early morning motorist had managed to swerve in time and brush past the top branches. The warden sighed. He knew that if the driver had driven carelessly or too fast and hit the tree, the popular outcry would have been against the elephant, not the bad driver.

The tracker led the game warden across the road to a plantation where Adam was quietly digging away at something in the ground. It was the first time the warden had ever seen an elephant among pine trees. He approached slowly, camera in hand, upwind and uphill. At last he was quite close and waited for Adam to lift his head so that his tusks would show clearly in the photograph.

Suddenly, to the warden's surprise and delight, a bushbuck stepped out of the high weeds and stood still, looking at him with what seemed mild astonishment.

This posed a problem. Of course, he wanted to get a shot of the bushbuck and the elephant together. As the warden stood rigid, for fear of scaring the buck, Adam raised his head. If the bushbuck was frightened by the click of the camera, would she dash off with her typical dog-like bark? And if so, would the elephant become more alert and annoyed? At last the picture was taken. Adam hadn't moved.

His arms were aching from holding the camera still so long. The warden lowered it and the bushbuck turned and trotted back into the shrubs. No bark, no sound at all.

He studied Adam through his binoculars. The elephant's tusks were long and yellow.

ELEPHANTS were once common in South Africa, but today you will find them only in the north of Zululand and the Transvaal lowveld, with a protected herd in the Addo Reserve and a small herd living wild in the ancient Knysna forests. There are, however, plans to introduce more elephants from the Kruger National Park into the Knysna forests so that the forest herds will increase.

The average height of an African elephant is 3,2 to 3,35 metres and a bull can weigh about six tons: he spends about 16 hours of each day eating and may consume up to 300 kilograms of food daily. Though the elephant walks about 10 kilometres per hour, it can charge at about 40 kilometres per hour when angered! Elephants live in herds, and mothers look after the calves for two years.

The tip of the left one was broken off. Most interesting was a hole in the top of his left ear: a neat round hole which could only have come from a bullet. So someone had taken a shot at him, probably some while before.

Adam's hump just brushed a trailing branch. The warden made a note of the tree and the next day, he measured the height. The elephant stood at 3,2 metres – no world record, but a fair-sized hunk of elephant by African standards.

He was certainly large enough to attract more photographers than merely the game warden. Some days later, two professional photographers arrived from Johannesburg to film the Knysna elephant. The warden agreed to help, but warned them that if Adam decided to charge, they must drop everything and run for their lives!

With the help of two trackers they managed to find Adam asleep under a tree. Their plan was simple. Pierre, with colour film in his camera, would move as close as possible with the warden, while Chris, with the camera with the black-and-white film, would photograph both of them and (hopefully) the elephant too.

Following a path through the forest, they all watched and listened carefully. The slightest noise might send the elephant either away from them or towards them! A glimpse of elephant hide showed in a shaft of sunlight peeping from between the leaves above.

The warden crept closer very quietly. He could see Adam's ears flapping against the afternoon heat. About 20 metres away, he stopped and examined the situation. By good fortune, Adam was facing in precisely the right direction. The first few paces he took would bring him on to the path, directly in view of the eager cameramen.

Back went the warden to where the photographers waited, loaded with heavy cameras and satchels of spare equipment. "Wait until he wakes up and steps out on to the path," he whispered. "But don't forget: if I say 'run', you run! Put your camera down if you have to. We can always fetch it later."

"I hope you're right," was the murmur from one of them.

Chris took up position on a high tree stump. Pierre and the warden moved ahead.

Adam had not moved. He stood there, swaying slightly. Pierre sighted his video camera and checked the focus. It seemed like years before Adam woke and decided to move.

There was no warning. There was Adam – much less than 25 metres away. Pierre pressed his button and a noise like a fairy football rattle came from his camera. It whirred remorselessly, and Adam swung to a halt, turned around and then charged towards them.

"Run!" urged the warden, and did so. Behind them came the rumbling thud of the elephant's feet. Ahead of them, Chris and the two trackers had disappeared into the forest.

They ran until they had no breath left in their lungs. Silence behind them. No elephant in sight. They paused for a cigarette and laughed together. Obviously, Adam had seen them retreat in such an undignified fashion, and was satisfied.

The next day they went back for the leather satchels full of equipment and spare reels of film. But Adam had found them and torn them to pieces. The camera was safe, though fragments of films and lenses were scattered far and wide.

"They seem to be such quiet creatures," said Chris to Pierre, thoughtfully.

"Now you know better," the warden advised them. "They are wild animals. And magnificent. May they stay with us a long time."

# JACK
## THE
# SIGNALMAN

The door of the railway cottage opened and a brownish-grey baboon came out, hurried to the pump in the garden and worked vigorously at the handle, pumping water into a bucket. Then he carried the bucket inside. A while later, the baboon reappeared and went over to where a light trolley stood beside the railway track. He pushed the trolley up until its front wheels touched the rails, then he sat back on his haunches, threw the wheels over the rail, gave the whole thing a twist and a push, and the trolley was ready to roll along the track.

"All ready, Jack?" called a voice from the cottage. Out came a man in railway uniform and flat, peaked cap. He moved awkwardly as both his legs ended in wooden pegs. He sat himself down on the trolley, wooden legs poking out at the front.

"Oh, bother!" said the man. "I've forgotten my stick."

The baboon hurried back to the cottage, came out with the walking stick, locked the front door and brought both stick and key to his master. Then the baboon gripped the back of the trolley with his forepaws, pushed strongly with his back feet and so propelled the signalman along the line to his signalbox.

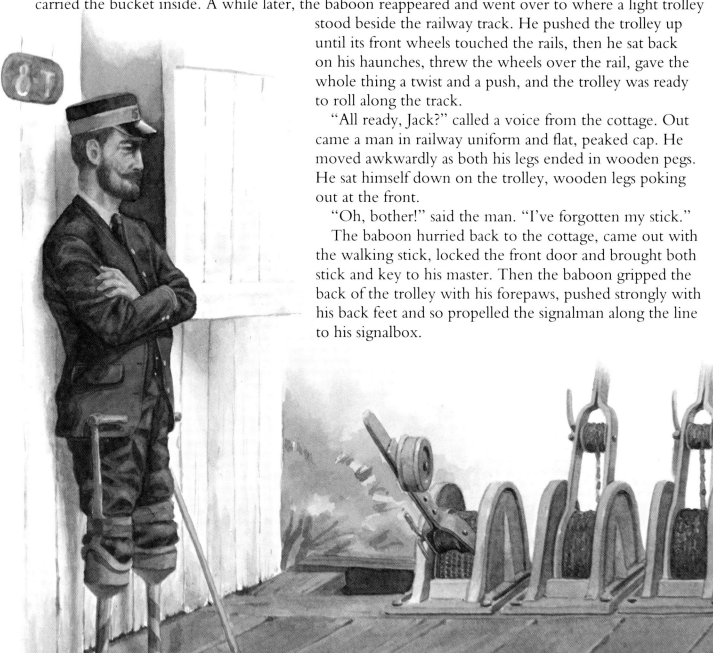

As James Edwin Wide travelled to work in this unusual fashion, he often thought back to that dreadful day in 1877 when he was helped out of Port Elizabeth hospital. He had been in despair. He had no faith in himself, few friends, and – worst of all – no legs. He had been a railway guard until a train had swept too close and knocked him down. All the railway officials could offer him at the time was the job of gatekeeper at a level crossing.

Moving about on his wooden legs to open gates and change the points had been so slow and painful that James had made himself this same light trolley which could run on the railway track. He had a big mongrel dog to pull the trolley, and found he could travel faster and easier that way. His confidence returned – and he was promoted to signalman at Uitenhage station.

That was when James saw a half-grown baboon for sale in the market near the station. The poor creature looked so forlorn that it reminded James of his own recent despair. He bought the baboon and named it Jack. It was the wisest thing James had ever done in his life. With a wide leather belt around its waist attached to a chain, Jack the baboon joined the dog in pulling the trolley along the rails. And when the dog was run over by a train, much the same way that James had been, Jack took over the trolley by himself. But there was one difference – he found it easier to push than to pull, so James took off Jack's chain and let him do just that. When they came to a downhill slope, Jack jumped joyously on the back of the trolley and the two of them skimmed along together!

One of James' duties as signalman was to take charge of the key of the padlock which locked points off the Graaff-Reinet line leading to the coal-yard. Puffing and blowing, the first morning train arrived, slowed down and gave the usual signal of four toots on the hooter to let James know that coal was wanted. Usually James hobbled into the signalbox, took the key from its nail on the wall, went out again and handed it to the driver as he steamed slowly past the platform.

But today Jack got there first. As soon as the four toots sounded, the baboon scampered inside, gripped with one hand on the top of the closed half-door to lift himself up, and grabbed the key with the other. Then he ran onto the platform and held out the key to the astonished train driver.

"That baboon your assistant, James?" he asked, laughing.

"Couldn't manage without him," answered James – and he knew that was the truth. "You're intelligent, aren't you, Jack? The best companion a man could have." He fondled the baboon tenderly and for a moment they seemed to cuddle each other. Jack knew his master was pleased, so he added this easy task to his other skills. From that day on, James never had to fetch the key again.

Of course, the main job of a signalman was to work the signals. Each lever in the signalbox was joined by a greased wire to its signal arm or junction point on the rails. It was hard work for a fit man; it was heavy work for a man with no legs. Even when no points had to be changed, there were 'distant' and 'home' signals to set for each train, and then they would have to be reset again afterwards.

After months of training the baboon, James knew that all he had to do was call out the name of the lever and Jack would instantly pull it. A whistle would be heard in the distance and Jack would spring to the correct 'home' signal while his master pulled on the heavier 'distant' signal lever. Once the train was past, Jack silently pushed his lever back into position and then chattered his delight as James patted him on the head.

"What's that flea-ridden ape doing in your signalbox?" rasped a voice from the doorway.

"He's helping with the signals," James explained mildly. "He's done it for months. I've been training him."

"Don't you dare do it again!" The burly foreman shook his fist at James. "I'll report you. I'll have you fired."

The threatening tone upset the baboon. He snarled, showing his heavy teeth, and ran at the foreman knocking him off balance.

"You hairy brute!" shouted the foreman. "I'll teach you!" But he was still on one leg as Jack charged him, shoulder to shoulder. The foreman staggered back and fell off the edge of the platform.

There were no trains near, but his dignity had been insulted. He seized a stick and climbed back onto the platform. As soon as he advanced on the baboon, Jack grabbed an empty coal sack and used it as a whip. Screaming with indignation, he beat the foreman with it so hard that clouds of black dust filled the air. With shouts of fury, the man retreated and stomped off, yelling promises of revenge.

James leant on the half-door of the signalbox and laughed until the tears streamed down his face.

"That'll teach the bully, won't it, Jack? I don't think he will report you. Otherwise he'll have to admit that you chased him away with a coal sack!"

The foreman must have said something, however, because soon there were official objections. "We can't have a mere animal operating such vital machinery! The passengers are protesting," said the Uitenhage station master. "What if there should be an accident?"

But there would be no accidents. Jack didn't make mistakes. James knew that or he wouldn't have trusted Jack the way he did.

However, James himself did make a mistake. One of the points had jammed. He hobbled his way over the rails to see what was wrong. A stone was caught in the gap. As James bent to take it out, his wooden peg-leg slipped on the gravel and he fell heavily, crushing his arm under him.

He lay there dazed, wondering if his arm was broken, and then became aware of a gentle hand stroking his face. It was Jack, whimpering as he pulled at James' body as if aware that it was dangerous to lie on the railway line.

"It's all right, Jack," he groaned. "I'm not dead. But I've hurt my arm badly. If the foreman finds out, he'll find a replacement for me at once and I'll lose my job for good. I've got to carry on. Jack, you'll have to do it for me until I'm better."

Jack nibbled gently at James' ear and appeared to understand. He helped his master to stand upright.

For the next three days, James lay on a mattress in a corner of the signalbox. At first he was in too much pain even to sit. Jack took over all his duties. He dashed out with the key when it was needed. He worked all the signal levers, even those for the distant signals. A little over a metre tall, he was strong enough to work the farthest signal about 1 200 metres away. Each evening he placed the trolley on the line, helped his master on to it and pushed him home to the little railway cottage. The next morning he brought him back to work.

On the fourth day a railway official in a smart blue coat glistening with gold braid appeared at the door. James was sitting on a stool but he was still unable to pull any of the levers.

"I have come to inform you that we have received a complaint," he said. As James started to explain about his injured arm, a train whistle blew in the distance, and Jack sprang into action, pulling exactly the correct signal levers. The official gaped as he watched. After the train had passed, there was a silence.

"I don't know what people are complaining about!" he muttered. "Seems to me that you and your...er...friend have everything completely under control. Well done!"

James smiled and smoothed down his heavy moustache. Of course there was no need for any alarm. Jack was the best friend he had ever had – and a darned good signalman as well!

It was the last time anyone complained. For nine years Jack gave the railway good and faithful service. The people who used the Uitenhage-Port Elizabeth line became very proud of their baboon signalman, but never so proud as James Edwin Wide himself.

BABOONS are often known by their Khoi name, Chacma. They live in troops all over southern Africa, provided there is food, water and either trees or rocks. Males can weigh as much as 44 kilograms and have a shoulder height of 80 centimetres. Because of their crop-raiding habits, we often forget the good baboons can do in the wild, particularly in controlling such insects as locusts. They have more intelligence than we sometimes are aware of. Eugene Marais, in his famous study *The Soul of the Ape,* found their mental processes so similar to ours that he could only compare chacma baboons to human standards.

# JOCK OF THE BUSHVELD

Five of the bull terrier puppies were fat, strong, yellow little chaps with dark muzzles – just like their father. The sixth was a poor, miserable, little rat of a thing. He was a sort of dirty, pale half-and-half colour, and he had a dark, sharp, wizened little muzzle. That was Jock.

The other puppies would tumble over him and take his food. They would bump into him when he was stooping over the dish of milk and porridge, and his head was so big and his legs so weak that he would topple over and fall head over heels into the dish. His master was always picking him out of the food and scraping it off him.

One of the oxen, sniffing around the transport riders' camp, came up to examine the puppy. It moved towards him slowly, giving big sniffs at this strange, new object. The puppy stood quite still with his stumpy tail cocked and his head a little to one side. When the huge ox's nose was near him he gave a sudden, short bark. The ox nearly tumbled over with fright. Even when the great mountain of a thing gave a clumsy plunge and trotted off, the puppy's tail and ears flickered for a second, but they stiffened up again instantly. With another of those sharp, little barks, he took a couple of steps forward and cocked his head to the other side. That was Jock's way.

And that was why young Percy FitzPatrick, living a hard life in the bush in the days when Pilgrim's Rest was full of gold-diggers, chose Jock as his dog. He was trained to lie down, to stay on guard, and not to touch food until his master had told him to 'take it'. Jock learned to obey hand signals too. Sometimes he pressed up against his master when he was aiming his gun at something. FitzPatrick would look at Jock, and Jock knew quite well what that meant. Down would go his ears and he would back away, drop his stump of a tail, wag it feebly and open his mouth into a sort of foolish laugh that was his apology. As he grew, he looked less rat-like and more handsome, with a smooth golden-brown coat and a white patch on his chest.

Jock's first experience of hunting was on a hot day when his master had

already shot at a steenbok and missed. As FitzPatrick sat in the shade of some thorn trees, a duiker stopped about 20 metres away. It was hardly possible to miss, so he aimed, fired and ran out after it, forgetting to take his gun with him.

Hit in the shoulder, the duiker stumbled, rolled over and over, then got up and dashed away on three legs. When he heard "After him, Jock," Jock was gone, taking a short cut to head it off. He caught up and jumped for its throat. The duiker, however, darted away, leaving him behind. By the time FitzPatrick caught up, Jock had a grip high on its back leg. Then the duiker fell, broke loose and thrust with its black spiky horns so swiftly that it seemed nothing could save Jock from being stabbed through and through. But if he could not catch the duiker, it would not catch him either.

On three legs, however, the duiker had no chance. In another minute Jock had it down again. FitzPatrick caught the struggling duiker by the head, held it down and tried to finish it with his knife. Neither man nor dog had learned yet what a buck can do with its hind legs. The supple body doubled up, and the hooves whizzed viciously by, striking the knife and sending it flying out of reach. With a sudden twist and a wrench, the duiker freed itself and was off again.

All this time Jock had been moving around, panting and licking his chops, longing to be at it again but not daring to join in without permission. When the duiker broke free, however, he waited for nothing and was on to it in one spring. He let go as it fell and, jumping free, had it by the throat before it could rise. Then it was his turn to learn the lesson of the duiker's feet.

The first kick went over his head and scraped harmlessly along his back. The second caught him on the shoul- der, and the razor-like toe cut his side open as if it had been

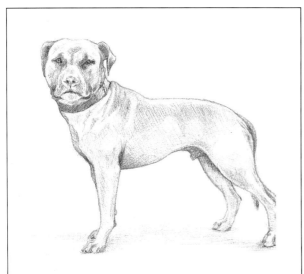

Although Jock is often described as a Staffordshire terrier, his mother, Jess, was in fact a BULL TERRIER. A bull terrier is a sturdy, heavily-built, smooth-coated breed of dog, usually white but sometimes brown. A cross between terrier and bulldog, they were originally bred for bull-baiting in England, so they make excellent hunting dogs.

slashed with a knife. Then Jock showed his pluck and cleverness. He never flinched or loosened his grip for a second. He swung his body clear of the whizzing feet and tugged away vigorously, keeping the buck's neck stretched out. The kicks grew weaker, the duiker slackened, and Jock had won.

He was just as happy as a dog could be, and perhaps he was proud of the wound that left a straight line from his shoulder to his hip – a memento of his first real hunt.

Jock's favourite method of attack was tugging sideways so that a buck crossed its legs and came down immediately; then he had it by the throat before it could rise again. Only once did he make a dreadful mistake; and he paid for it – very nearly with his own life.

Jock was with FitzPatrick in a grove of bushy, wild plums when suddenly they stood face to face with a grand kudu bull less than a dozen metres away. Huge spiral horns and wide staring eyes – followed by a whirlwind of dust and leaves as it turned and fled. FitzPatrick fired hurriedly, and the great creature sank for a moment, almost to the ground. Then it struck up the slope, as FitzPatrick fired again and again – but each time a longer shot. He sent Jock on and followed as fast as he could.

FitzPatrick's old Martini rifle had one bad fault: it was always jamming. Unless the cartridges were kept well greased, the empty shells would stick. It jammed then, and all he could do was run on, towards Jock and the kudu.

The kudu's leg was broken, but his nimbleness was still astonishing. Knowing every trick of attack and defence, he was blazing with anger at this persistent little gadfly that worried him so and kept out of reach. He would back slowly, to tempt the dog on; then with a sudden lunge the great horns swished through the spot where Jock had been only a fraction of a second before.

Perhaps realising that attack from the front was useless, Jock went for the broken leg. He got a hold and dragged it back along the ground. The kudu tried to regain its footing, was tripped by its crossed legs and came down with a crash. As it fell, Jock shot around and fastened onto its nose. But this was no duiker, impala or rietbok. The kudu gave a snort of indignation and flung him off, sending him skidding along the ground.

Jock raced in again with head down and the little eyes black with fury. He was too mad to be wary and the long horns swung around with a swish. One black point seemed to pierce him through and through, showing clear out the other side, and a twist of the great head sent him twirling high up into the air. It had just missed him, passing under his stomach. He dropped with a thud, scrambled to his feet and raced in again.

Once more he fastened on the nose only to be shaken worse than before. The kudu literally flogged the ground with him. As FitzPatrick still wrestled with his rifle, he had to shut his eyes for it seemed as if the plucky dog would be beaten into pulp. Setting his foot against a tree, FitzPatrick wrenched until the empty cartridge flew out.

Reloading fast, he came around to within a metre of where Jock stood firm under the trunk of a tree, still hanging on to the kudu's nose. The hauling kudu seemed to stretch Jock's neck visibly. But the rifle shot was the end. As the splendid head dropped slowly over, Jock let go his hold.

He had not uttered a sound except the grunts that were knocked out of him.

Half-way between the Crocodile and Komati rivers, there are half a dozen small koppies with rich grasslands between. Where his master took cover by crawling, Jock felt the need to see what was ahead. As the grass was too high for him to see over, he took jumps of increasing strength. At the top of his jump his legs were all bunched up, his eyes staring eagerly and his ears flapped out giving him a look of comic astonishment.

That was how he spotted the string of kudu. FitzPatrick got in one shot before they cantered away. The last of the troop, a big cow, stumbled but cantered on. By then, Jock was close behind. He may have thought there was a broken leg to grip – or perhaps he was just too bold. Anyway, he jumped at one of the hind legs, and at the same moment the kudu lashed out viciously. One foot struck him under the jaw close to the throat, whipped his head back, and sent him spinning through the air.

He lay limp and motionless, with blood oozing from his mouth and nose. FitzPatrick felt desperately for his heart-beat and called, "Jock!" again and again. Remembering a nearby pool, he filled his hat with water and poured it over the limp dog. He dribbled water into Jock's mouth, as he pressed the dog's sides to try and restore his breathing.

The old hat was leaky, and FitzPatrick was returning for a second hatful when he saw Jock roll over, his head shaking in a dazed manner and his eyes blinking. At the touch of a hand, his ears moved up and the stumpy tail scraped feebly in the dead leaves. He took no notice when FitzPatrick called his name, for he was stone deaf. From that day on, he depended on signals, for he never heard another sound. This deafness didn't seem to worry him in the veld, but it became dangerous for Jock in camp. He would take a snooze on the warm earth of the track and several times was nearly run over by a wagon. Meanwhile, to earn his living, Percy FitzPatrick was forced to make long treks to Mozambique. For a while he left Jock in the care of an old friend, Tom Barnett, who kept a trader's store. FitzPatrick never saw his dog again.

One bright, moonlit night, Tom was aroused by a clatter of falling boxes and the wild cries of his chickens in the fenced-off yard. He grabbed his rifle, opened the little window which gave him a view of the chicken house and waited for the thief to appear. Then the dim form of a dog appeared in the doorway. Tom lifted the gun slowly and took careful aim.

When the smoke cleared away, the figure of the dog lay still. Tom went back to bed, satisfied.

In the morning, Tom pushed open the reed gate and made his way towards the chicken house. Under the porch where the sunlight touched it, something shone like polished gold.

Jock lay stretched out on his side – he might have been asleep. But on the snow-white chest there was one red spot. And inside the chicken house lay the thieving mongrel dog – dead. Jock had done his duty.

# HUBERTA
## THE
## HIPPO

Take a visit to the Kaffrarian Museum in King William's Town and you will be able to view the heaviest heroine of all time! Huberta stands firmly among the other large mammals, her wanderings behind her now. (At the start of her travels, people thought she was male. 'Hubert the Hippo' said the first newspaper reports, until somebody realised that was wrong and changed her nickname to Huberta.) Groups of hikers today are fond of hiking trails. To cover 1 600 kilometres along the coast of Africa, taking nearly three years over it, would be quite a journey! Yet that is what Huberta did – all by herself.

Some sunny day in November 1928, Huberta left her lagoon home in Zululand and started to munch her way through the sugar cane fields. For a while, she lived in a pool near the railway line. The trains slowed down as they passed so that everyone could get a better view, and passengers even threw fruit to her.

Why did she start her travels? Nobody knows. But once the newspapers started writing about her, she became famous. After that the crowds never left her alone. So she probably kept on the move in search of peace and quiet.

On a warm January evening in 1929, a garage-owner was driving home near Tongaat when he found a narrow bridge blocked by a large animal. Huberta, disturbed by the glaring headlights, stared at the car and then decided she didn't like it. She walked haughtily away and then headed towards the nearest lagoon.

Natal had a new tourist attraction! People hired buses and crashed their way through the bushes to catch a glimpse of Huberta. Several took one look at her huge tusks and cavernous mouth and retreated hastily. She was, after all, a wild animal. For a month she stayed in the cool waters of the Umhlanga Lagoon. Then she went travelling again and arrived in Durban.

The Durban Country Club, with its golf course alongside, was a place for well-dressed diners and polite conversation as a rule. But the rules were broken on the last night of March when Huberta peered through the main gate. The Club steward saw her and reported it. Shrieks and squeals of excitement brought everyone running. Huberta retreated fast towards the tenth hole. The humans followed. Gentlemen in bow ties and dinner jackets, ladies in long dresses and high-heeled shoes, waiters in crisp uniforms – all went charging over the golf course after the frightened hippo. Sensibly, she hid in some bushes. Her pursuers got bored with searching and went back to the Club for a last drink.

It was still dark the following morning – April 1st – when she reappeared in the middle of Durban. A wide-eyed ricksha-puller discovered her huge hippopotamus bulk, lit up red, green and blue from the neon lights, outside the West Street Pharmacy. It was the most impressive April Fool's Day joke he had ever seen! But Huberta was far too large and real. He swung his feathered bicycle-carriage around and fled.

Concrete and tarmac was no home for a hippo, however. When early morning crowds started to gather where Huberta stood solidly across the tramlines outside the Federal Hotel, she beat a retreat through Victoria Park. From there, she was glad to find her way back to the Umgeni River mouth and submerge herself in its cool waters.

After that, the hunt was on in earnest. Reporters wanted to catch the latest story, photographers wanted to catch her on film, zoo-keepers wanted to catch her. The Natal provincial council also reminded the public that hippos were 'royal game', and could not be shot or captured without a special permit. So Huberta was protected even by the law.

As she fled from river to river, moving along the Natal south coast towards Transkei, she was greeted with more than mere popularity. The Zulus wondered if she was in some way connected with the spirit of Shaka. Near Bendigo, the Indians declared her 'the Protector of the Poor'. *The Star* reported how "Sacrificial fires were lighted and peace offerings made to Huberta". On the Wild Coast, the Pondos were worried that she might represent the spirit of a famous sangoma, so they dared not stop her munching through their maize fields.

By now Huberta had gained world fame. A poem about the persecuted hippo appeared in the London magazine *Punch*. Newspapers in England, America, India, Egypt and Australia carried details of her travels. It was happily predicted that she would arrive in Cape Town in time for Christmas.

By March 1930, she had reached the pretty village of Port St Johns and decided to stay. For six months she wallowed happily in the river and feasted in the gardens on either side. Though the river's name, Mzimvubu, means 'home of the hippos', no hippopotamus had been seen there in living memory. But Huberta was quite content in her new home.

When the weather became warmer, Huberta moved again – past the rocky headlands of the Wild Coast towards the farming country around East London. By day she hid in the river valleys, by night she selected choice plants and vegetables from farms and gardens. Huberta's fate was argued out in the newspaper columns. Farmers threatened to shoot her if she broke any more fences and ate their crops. Letters begged the authorities to capture Huberta for her own safety, for several zoos were eager to secure such a famous resident. Other letters deplored the idea that such a free, roaming animal should be confined to a cage. As more attempts were made to catch her, so Huberta was continually forced to move on.

A HIPPOPOTAMUS (the word means 'river horse') can weigh as much as 1 500 kilograms and stands approximately 1,5 metres at the shoulder. A hippo needs to live in water, otherwise its skin will dry out. However, hippos seldom stay submerged for more than two or three minutes at a time. They are active at night, resting during the day. They usually stay within or around their chosen territory, which they defend vigorously if they have young calves. Their huge jaws are quite able to bite a crocodile in half!

There was even a report that, exhausted by her travels, she went to sleep on the railway line near East London. The engine driver blew his whistle loudly, and as Huberta failed to wake, gave her a gentle nudge with the 'cow-catcher' front of the engine. She snorted her protests, rose indignantly to her feet and lumbered away. That, at least, was the story the engine driver told the newspapers!

In April 1931, the poor tired hippopotamus was taking refuge in the Keiskamma River near Peddie. There, a farmer's son saw the tracks of a large animal in his garden. With his father and brother, he followed the spoor and spotted some creature in the river spouting water through its nostrils. The three of them opened fire and shot every time it rose to the surface. Bleeding badly but still alive, Huberta moved away. The next morning, the farmer found her again and fired twice with his rifle. That ended her suffering.

# THE
# FAMOUS
# SOMERSET

This is almost more of a detective story than an animal story, but that makes it all the more exciting. There was a horse called Somerset and he *was* famous – exactly what for you must decide yourself.

George Jameson, a successful Durban businessman, was deeply in love with Pauline. She loved him too, and particularly adored his skill in storytelling. He told pioneering tales of his father Charles Jameson who had trekked up the Drakensberg in 1838, and stirring adventures of his father's friend Jan Hofmeyr, but above all she liked most the story of the horse Somerset. So who is to blame George if he embroidered the story a little? All good stories grow in the telling!

He told how, when Jan Hofmeyr was preparing to join the Great Trek, he knew that he needed a strong, sturdy horse. So he exchanged his farm land, which he was leaving behind, for cattle and a good hunter. "Steady as a rock, old boy," declared the retired English officer whose horse it was. "You won't find a better horse anywhere. Trained in the military riding school. He's called Somerset – after our Governor, Lord Charles Somerset."

Though Jan had no love for the British Governor, he examined the bay horse and agreed it was a fine animal. Standing fifteen hands high, Somerset had a small head like an Arab's, a satin smooth coat like a cloth of gold. He had a flowing black mane and dark stripes on his forequarters.

The other Boers on trek admired the horse too. He was as mild-mannered as any pet, yet fast enough to run down an ostrich and trained to ignore gunfire. So when Jan found himself inside the Boer laager at the Battle of Blood River, he was proud to lend Somerset to their commandant, Andries Pretorius. After the Zulus had made countless attacks and failed to penetrate the gun-defended laager, it was on Somerset that Pretorius galloped out at the head of his few hundred horsemen. They met determined resistance from the Zulu warriors, but after three sorties they turned the victory into an overwhelming defeat.

"You should have seen him, my darling!" said George, making most of it up as he went along. "His eyes full of fire, his girth deep, his forelegs straight! As I saw Pretorius gallop out, elephant gun in hand, coatless, sjambok on his wrist and bending over Somerset's neck, I knew there was never a smarter soldier."

With Dingaan's army scattered, the Boers began to settle on the land they had won. But when the British reoccupied Natal in 1842, Andries Pretorius gathered the Boer commandos to drive them out and Jan once again lent him the horse Somerset. The Boers camped at Congella, besieging the British troops in the fort. Many eyes admired the fine bay horse. So it was hardly surprising that one dark night a Griqua crept into the Boer laager and, pretending he was a servant, quietly untied the rein and led Somerset away into the British camp where they gladly bought the horse from him.

The British, desperately short of supplies, needed to send a message asking for relief. It was Dick King who volunteered to make the ride. And it was here that George's storytelling ran away with him. According to the story he told Pauline, Dick King rode Somerset all the way to Grahamstown, both of them arriving exhausted.

"What became of Somerset?" asked Pauline.

George replied, "The news in the military barracks the next morning was that King lay in the hospital and Somerset was dead."

It made a great ending to a good story – and that's the way that it has gone into the history books. However, George Jameson wasn't there with Dick King, and someone else was. Dick himself never spoke about his famous ride in later years, but the Zulu who rode with him part of the way did record his memories. Ndongeni twice dictated his version of what had happened.

He remembered clearly how they "started off at midnight, King riding a white horse and I a bay one." Now, Somerset was not a white horse! As a good detective, what can you deduce from the

clues? Surely, that if Somerset did indeed take part in that famous ride, it was Ndongeni who rode him and not Dick King!

So let's leave George telling tall stories to his adoring Pauline and find out what really happened to the famous Somerset.

Dick King was certainly the best man in the British camp to attempt to get the vital message through. Four years before, when news reached the English at Port Natal of a threatened Zulu attack on the Boer trekkers, Dick had set off on foot and covered the 192 kilometres in four days and four nights. He arrived just too late to save Retief's camp, but he walked on a further 16 kilometres and reached Gerrit Maritz in time to help him form a laager and defend it.

On the night of 25 May 1842, the Cato brothers helped King and Ndongeni cross Durban Bay in a rowing boat with two army horses swimming behind – one of which could well have been Somerset. King mounted the white horse and Ndongeni was on the bay riding a saddle without stirrups. They rode through the night to avoid being seen. They crossed rivers close to the sea, because they feared the Boers might be guarding the normal river crossings further inland. Dick King swam across each river in his shirt, while Ndongeni (who could not swim) kept King's clothes and clutched his horse's mane. Ndongeni remembered how his bay horse "was very frisky, and inclined to leap where less powerful animals would only walk or wade". That certainly sounds like the Somerset we have come to know.

LORD CHARLES SOMERSET, Governor of the Cape between 1814 and 1817 after whom Dick King's famous horse was named, was a keen importer of thoroughbred horses to the Cape.

A true thoroughbred is descended from one of three particular Arab sires and 50 chosen English mares. As the horse, Somerset, is described as having had an Arab head, it is quite possible that he might even have been bred from the horses brought to the Cape colony by his namesake, Lord Charles.

At a British military camp by the Umgazi mouth, Ndongeni was provided with stirrups and a fresh horse. His legs, however, had become so sore that a few days later he had to turn back. Dick went on alone. He knew the mission stations ahead (having been a wagon driver over that area for many years) and planned to call there, as he knew that one horse could not go all the way. We know that he changed horses at Buntingville and then again at Butterworth. So he certainly did not cruelly ride one horse to death. He did, however, get through to Grahamstown only ten days after leaving Port Natal, having covered about 960 kilometres. Soon he was on his way back, travelling with relief troops and supplies, and fully deserves his fame as 'saviour of Natal'. Ndongeni was on the shore watching his master's triumphant return.

So what happened to Somerset? If he was one of the horses supplied at the start of the ride, then he must have been replaced at the Umgazi mouth. Duly rested, as an army horse he would have been returned to Port Natal, and there appears to be evidence that he ended his days on King's sugarcane farm at Isipingo. We shall never know for sure – but it seems a kinder fate for 'the famous Somerset'.

# SMURF
## AND
# HENRY

"Save Smurf and Henry!" *The Cape Times* was the first to print the story. Soon United Press International, *Die Burger*, the *Daily Telegraph* in London, and even the American Broadcasting Corporation from Detroit were scrambling to cover the pathetic tale of two lovers about to be parted by heartless officials. All the stranger, because the lovebirds were just that – a penguin and a pelican!

The young jackass penguin had been starving and sick with enteritis when Walter Mangold first saw him. Without proper treatment, the bird was going to die. So the penguin, soon named Smurf, was nursed back to health and made its home in Walter's bird sanctuary, the World of Birds. Smurf enjoyed his new life and quickly learned to parade for meals outside the kitchen at precisely the right time each day.

Henry should actually have been called Henrietta as she was female. She had been brought to the park with a badly broken wing and was one of hundreds of birds treated and cared for by Walter Mangold and his team. Unable to fly, the pelican adapted happily to life on ground level – and there she met Smurf. Quite simply, they 'fell in love'.

From then on, visitors to the World of Birds delighted in watching them. Henry would wrap her long bill round Smurf's tubby body and stand happily as cameras clicked at close range. They had another pose too: with Smurf's head actually inside the pelican's large beak. The birds were completely tame and accepted humans without complaint, even when Henry was referred to as a 'perlemoen' instead of a pelican! When Henry wandered away with her long, slow, well-measured steps, Smurf would try desperately to keep up. His staggering waddle made him look almost drunk.

The World of Birds wildlife sanctuary nestles in the steep-sided green valley of Hout Bay on the Cape Peninsula. All the correct permits are applied for to keep their vast collection of over three thousand birds, as well as smaller animals like bushbabies, monkeys and tortoises. Penguins, however, need special permission. So Walter Mangold was horrified to receive a letter from the Department of Nature Conservation.

"I regret to inform you", said the letter, "that your application to keep two jackass penguins in captivity was not successful. The alarming decline in the number of penguins along our coast has resulted in a departmental policy decision not to allow healthy penguins to be kept in captivity and they must, therefore, be rehabilitated and returned to the sea. Under the circumstances you are advised to contact SANCCOB to collect the birds before 15 January 1981 in order to rehabilitate the birds and release them".

The letter arrived on a Friday afternoon. That left only three days in which to do anything. One of the penguins was duly returned to its natural environment, but surely not Smurf? Smurf was tame – he had lost his ability to survive in the sea. To return him to such an unfamiliar life would be an act of cruelty, not compassion. Walter Mangold didn't know what to do.

Then *The Cape Times* heard of the story. They printed the details on Monday and, within a day, both the World of Birds and the Department of Nature Conservation had received countless indignant telephone calls. Wisely, Walter phoned the government department and spoke to the Deputy Director. Such problems are always best handled personally. They both agreed that the matter was getting out of hand.

The Deputy Director promised to pay an official visit to examine the merits of this special case. His shiny car duly drew up outside the World of Birds. The important official walked slowly up the

twisting paths, where bright parrots screamed from their perches, and through the large walk-through aviaries. He seemed increasingly impressed by what he saw. Walter was beside him, his heart pounding. Would the required permission be given or not?

Finally they encountered the ill-fated pair – Smurf and Henry, who were not at all flustered by their important visitor. They just wanted to stay friends and stay together – and the Deputy Director smiled and agreed that they should.

The news was flashed round the world by television, radio and newspapers. "Official: Smurf and Henry can live together." The contented birds filled the prime spot on the evening news. Even more visitors flocked to the World of Birds to see the remarkable pair. Henry played with her ball and gulped down whole pilchards. Smurf waddled quite happily alongside.

The WHITE PELICAN is a large bird with a pouch under its long beak, and lives in flocks along the south-western coast and off Natal. During the breeding season its white feathers take on a pinkish colour. They hatch their chalky white eggs on the ground in untidy nests made of seaweed and feathers.

The JACKASS PENGUIN gets its name from its cry which sounds like the braying of a donkey. Black-backed with a dark line down each side of its white chest, the jackass penguin usually breeds in colonies on coastal islands, digging burrows in the hard sand or among rocky boulders. Penguin nests are often lined with old feathers and dry seaweed.

In the springtime, Henry (or Henrietta) was transformed from a blushing teenager to a desirable young lady as her plumage made the normal changes of her breed. The skin on her face and bill shone a waxy off-white, touched in places with a peachy pink. She clamoured for the attention of the bird handlers and especially of Smurf.

The love story could have ended there. But 'the eternal love triangle' can occur, even with birds!

A few months later, a rare white jackass penguin was found on a False Bay beach. She was clogged with oil and moulting badly. Restored to health at the World of Birds, the white penguin wandered around and soon met and fell in love with Smurf. Henry didn't really mind and even played with the newcomer. Then Smurf seemed to decide that his previous 'mixed marriage' might not work out, so he started paying more attention to his new companion. Luckily, a very handsome male pelican arrived at the sanctuary with an injured wing and stole Henry's heart.

So Henry and Smurf parted as friends, and today they still see each other from time to time.

# THE FISH WITH FOUR LEGS

"You know I don't want to be interrupted. I have all these university exam papers to mark." Professor JLB Smith of the chemistry department at Rhodes University was understandably annoyed. But the bulky packet that had arrived by post caught his interest.

It had been sent to him by the director of the East London Museum, Miss Marjorie Courtenay-Latimer. A keen student of matters relating to fish, Prof Smith had often helped out at the museum. Now his friend had sent him drawings of a strange fish she had seen amongst the catch of a trawler in East London. It was a large fish, over a metre in length, of a strange purple-blue colour. Could he help identify it? she asked. He examined her drawings with amazement. They were like no fish that he had ever seen before!

But the exam papers still had to be marked, so it was six weeks before Prof Smith could visit East London to see the fish for himself. By then, it had been stuffed and mounted, and its soft insides thrown away. Its blue scales had turned a shiny brown from the preservation process and four stubby fins stuck out from its heavy body, almost like stunted legs. He stared at it, compared notes from books on prehistoric creatures and eventually looked at Miss Courtenay-Latimer, amazed.

"This fish ceased to exist millions of years ago – or so we all believed. It is a coelacanth. It has to be. A live coelacanth!" Prof Smith beamed with delight. "At least, it was alive when it was caught. Oh, what a pity you couldn't preserve its insides so we could know what it ate and how it lived."

Scientists all over the world were astounded when the discovery of the coelacanth was made public. The story of 'the living fossil' appeared in newspapers, and everyone asked the same question: were there more? Prof Smith asked fishermen along South Africa's eastern ports to watch out for the strange fish. Nobody found one.

The next year, 1939, the Second World War started and newspapers had grimmer stories to print than vague hopes of catching prehistoric fish. But Prof Smith hadn't forgotten. Some scientists guessed that as the coelacanth hadn't been seen or caught before, it must live in deep waters. Prof Smith studied the coelacanth very carefully and disagreed with them. It looked far more like a shallow-water fish. Where could it have come from? He decided it might have come from the coast of East Africa or Madagascar.

In 1950, he tried to organise an official fishing expedition to search for coelacanth in the tropical Indian Ocean but his plans were not accepted. So he and his wife went on expeditions of their own. He had leaflets printed in English, French and Portuguese, with a picture of the coelacanth, offering £100 reward. A fair sum in those days!

Towards the end of 1952, Prof Smith had only been home a few hours after his latest expedition when a telegram arrived from a Captain Hunt. He sailed a fishing schooner and had been interested to hear of Smith's search. His crew had caught a large fish off the Comores, a group of islands between Madagascar and Mozambique, and he was convinced it was a coelacanth.

How could Smith get there? There was no air service. A boat would take weeks. By the time he arrived, the body of the fish may have rotted and those important internal organs would be lost again, and he would have to start his search all over again.

In vain, Prof Smith tried to find some way of flying to the Comores. But it was the Christmas holidays and nobody seemed very interested in his search for a fish which was thought to be extinct for thousands of years. He contacted everyone he could think of and even phoned important government ministers. But he met with no success. People were either too busy enjoying their

The COELACANTH is a large fish which was quite common about 250 million years ago. Fossils of this fish have been found, and it was thought to have become extinct 60 million years ago. Its Latin name is *Latimeria chalumnae* in honour of a past director of the East London museum, Miss Marjorie Courtenay-Latimer, who first noted its appearance in modern times. Attention has recently been focused on diving expeditions in South African waters, where it is predicted that coelacanth are living at deep levels.

holiday or simply not interested. Eventually, quite late in the evening, he phoned the Prime Minister himself. Dr DF Malan was on holiday at his seaside house in the Strand, and he was already in bed. His wife took the call but refused to disturb him and said she would tell him in the morning. Prof Smith put the phone down and, without much hope, sat back with a cup of tea.

However, Dr Malan had heard the telephone ring and he insisted his wife tell him about the matter. He knew of the professor and by luck Smith's book, *Sea Fishes of Southern Africa*, was in the house. The Prime Minister read the section on the coelacanth carefully. Then he said, "The man that wrote this book would not ask my help at a time like this unless it was desperately important. I must speak to him".

So, despite his wife's protests, Dr Malan phoned Smith at 10.30 pm that same night. Prof Smith explained urgently the significance of the coelacanth catch and the need to reach the Comores as soon as possible. This was a matter of importance to the world and South African pride was at stake.

The voice through the phone said, "I must congratulate you on your Afrikaans. It is excellent".

There was a long pause while Prof Smith sat and hoped. Then the Prime Minister told him that he would arrange for a military plane first thing in the morning.

So, a dazed Prof Smith reached the Comores in a military Dakota, where the captain who had sent the telegram met him with the words. "Don't worry, it's a coelacanth all right!" And it was.

A large coffin-like box was opened and at first all Smith could see was a mass of cotton wool. Suppose they were wrong? Suppose he had flown all this way on a false alarm? Then as they uncovered the fish, he saw the bony head, the large purple-blue scales, the spiny fins. Prof Smith found tears splashing on his hands as he knelt beside the box and realised that he was crying.

There, in front of him, was a creature as rare as a dinosaur – a fish which had survived unchanged since the days of the dinosaurs. As the newspapers had called it, those years before, 'a living fossil'.

Prof Smith had discovered the home of the coelacanths. Since then, several more of these strange 'four-legged' fish have been caught off the Comores. The local fishermen don't find that strange at all. They've been catching coelacanths for hundreds of years!

# Eric the Penguin

When he first forced his way out of his shell, Eric didn't see rocks and waves as most penguins do. He saw concrete and wire pens and a small chlorinated pool. He had been hatched inside one of the sheltered pens looked after by SANCCOB – the South African National Foundation for the Conservation of Coastal Birds.

No doubt, as he grew from a greyish fledgling into a mature black and white jackass penguin, his parents told him how lucky they were to have been brought to this place of safety. Along with hundreds of other penguins, they had been caught in an oil slick which made their feathers waterlogged. They could have drowned or died from the cold. Fortunately, one of the many SANCCOB-approved bird watchers along the coast rescued the penguins and arranged for them to be taken to the facilities at Rietvlei. There, they were hosed down, given a numbered identification tag on the left flipper, and washed over and over with warm water and a gentle cleansing fluid. Feeding was a problem. Eric's parents liked live fish not dead ones! However, there was no way hundreds of injured birds could dive after live fish in the small SANCCOB pools, so they had to be happy being fed by hand.

Eric's parents were among the lucky ones. A hundred years ago there were jackass penguins all round our coasts, from Algoa Bay to Walvis Bay. In those days, a coastal island such as Dassen Island was home to millions of penguins. Half a million penguin eggs were taken off the island each year. Today there may be only a few hundred penguins on the island. At least three quarters of our entire penguin population have been killed off during this century alone. The jackass penguin (so called by Vasco da Gama because 'they bray like asses') is one of our most endangered sea birds. Its natural enemies, such as sharks and seals, were replaced by Man. Even though early European settlers disliked the salted, oily taste of penguin flesh, they were quite willing to eat penguin eggs. The hunt for bird droppings, called guano, for use as fertilizer destroyed sheltered breeding grounds. Islands such as these are protected areas today, but sadly nothing protects our sea birds from oil pollution or spinning propeller blades.

53

As Eric grew up under the shade netting and wad-dled his way from one concrete-lined pen to another, he saw other birds as well. Handsome blue-eyed Cape gannets squabbled by the water, and seagulls with injured wings sat thoughtfully waiting for the day when they could fly again. He might have tried to make friends with a cormorant or a huge yellow-billed albatross being cared for at the SANCCOB centre. His growth was recorded and checked regularly by the staff. Eric quite enjoyed his sheltered way of life, though somewhere at the back of his mind was an idea that he could probably be enjoying a much wider world than this.

He experienced the awkward time of moult, when penguins stand around on shore for up to three weeks, waiting for the new crop of feathers to grow. They cannot eat at all during that time, because they cannot swim without their self-oiled, water-resistant plumage. Eric grew his new coat of feathers without any trouble – and there was food available if he want-ed it. Known as one of their 'baby blues', he was watched with particular interest by the staff.

So it was both exciting and frightening when, at six months old, he was put through yet another inspec-tion. He was examined all over, checked for healthy plumage, marked on the list 'for release' and placed inside plastic crates with a batch of other penguins. It was all rather undignified, Eric thought. Then they were on their way, driven by lorry and ferried by ship to Robben Island. To be welcomed ashore by the S.A. Prison Service is a fate that many of us would wish to avoid. But for Eric it was one step towards freedom.

He looked around at the rocks and the bare sandy shore beyond. There were no dogs around or people to make him nervous. When the lid was lifted off, he sniffed at the sea air and clambered out. The older birds, born in the wild and glad to return, rushed eagerly to the sea, dived in and swam happily away.

Eric stopped. This vast stretch of heaving water didn't look anything like the pool he was used to. Sure, he had learned how to dive and how to stand up for himself among the other birds. But, this ...! There were strange birds here, too: ones without little tags on their flippers. He peered around anxiously,

## The Work of SANCCOB

*The South African National Foundation for the Conservation of Coastal Birds was launched in 1968 after the German tanker* Esso Essen *struck a rock off the Cape Peninsula, and released some 15 000 tons of crude oil into the sea. About 3 000 oiled penguins and 500 gannets were rescued from the spill and nobody knew where to take them or how to treat them. The SPCA did its best but it just could not cope with the huge numbers. Althea Westphal ended up with hundreds at her home in Newlands where they were washed in the bath. Today, SANCCOB has a centre at Rietvlei specially built to treat 2 000 oiled birds, but still relies heavily on contributions from the public and voluntary workers to help the small professional team. If you wish to contact them, the address is: SANCCOB, P.O.Box 11116, Bloubergrant, 7443.*

paused, waddled a few paces, sniffed and stopped again. Then he took heart. After all, what would Dad say if he came back home again without having tried out the real live sea!

He put his head up proudly, held his jet-black flippers out for balance, and started his way down to the water. Eric plunged joyously and swam out swiftly to sea. Hey! It was fabulous in the waves! He didn't even give as much as a backward glance at the SANCCOB staff who had watched him so anxiously. Eric was the sixteenth penguin born in captivity which they had tended and helped to grow. He had become quite a favourite of theirs.

'Where's Eric?' asked a girl the next day, one of the visiting party of school children. They had heard of him too. The SANCCOB supervisor explained that Eric had grown up strong and sensible enough to be released into the sea world where he belonged. The children watched and learned what people are doing to destroy so many of the creatures of earth and sea – and what some of mankind, like those at SANCCOB, are doing to save a little of what is left.

# The heroine of Goudini

'No, that's definitely the one I want,' insisted young Rian Huisamen. The mare was the wildest of the bunch, but the 11-year-old boy had been promised a horse of his own for a long time and so was quite sure of his choice. At first, they couldn't even catch her, she was so swift on her feet. But, the little brown mare, Beauty, soon settled in happily at Witrivier farm at Goudini Road (near Rawsonville in the Cape mountains) which the Huisamen family were steadily rebuilding.

The farm was as wild as the horse! Wattle and Port Jackson trees grew unrestrained beside the stony Du Toit River and around the dilapidated farm buildings. Every weekend, Johan and Fenna Huisamen and their two young sons, Henti and Rian, drove to Witrivier and did a little more restoration to the old farmhouse. The farm seemed to have everything: chickens, geese, sheep, cattle, horses, and even an ostrich! Rian and Henti enjoyed every minute of their weekends, though there was lots of work to be done as well.

One wet and cold Sunday in June 1993, snow tipped the mountain tops and heavy rains had turned the river into a churning, muddy torrent. Before breakfast, Johan and Fenna decided to check on the horses. One of them, a Palomino mare, was about to have a foal. They drove round by the road bridge above their property because the horses were in the paddock on the far side of the river. The water was running far too strongly for them to wade across as they usually did. Grandfather Hank Gorter decided to go too, so both boys pulled on their yellow oilskin suits and climbed into the bakkie.

When they reached the paddock, Beauty heard their footsteps and came out to meet them through the pouring rain. Her chestnut foal, Sultan, only four days old, looked soaked and cold.

'Rian,' said his father, 'quickly put a halter on Beauty. Then we can lead her back to the farm.'

Huddled under his rainproof hood, Rian was glad that his own special horse and her foal would soon be safe inside the sheltering stable.

But the horses were quite used to taking the short cut to the farm across the river. The two mares and the stallion promptly sprang into the water. The river was running stronger than anyone realised. They reached the far bank, but had to battle, chest-deep, against the current. Even the stallion lost his footing and was rolled over by the water a few of times.

'Stay, Beauty!' shouted Rian, over the roar of the river, and his father tried to hold her back. But the mare had a mind of her own, and plunged into the water with her foal. Rian watched anxiously, as they fought their way across. Beauty nudged her foal on, and stayed downstream of him all the way to steady his small body against the swirling current.

'They're there!' cried his mother out aloud, and Rian sighed with relief as he watched Beauty scramble determinedly up the far bank.

Suddenly, as the foal struggled on the slippery stones, he slipped and fell back into the river. The current was far stronger than the little foal, and he was swept away. Without hesitating, Beauty jumped back in and swam after her foal.

The current carried the terrified foal back across the river, towards where Rian and his family were standing. Grandfather Hank pushed young Henti aside and reached out to grab the foal as it whirled past. But the raging water had cut under the bank where he was standing, and it collapsed. Out of his depth immediately, Hank was still trying to catch hold of the frightened foal. It was impossible. The torrent of icy water carried him past – far out of reach.

Rian watched in horror as the foal and then his grandfather were swept away by the water. His mother jumped forward, lost her footing too, and was lucky to snatch a branch or she would have gone too. But his grandfather and the two horses were now out of sight, in the pouring rain and the angry river.

So Rian never saw how his horse swam to the rescue. Beauty headed first for Grandfather Hank and pushed him towards the bank. She wasn't gentle and neither was the river. Hank ended up clutching the roots of an upturned tree, frozen, soaked, and with a couple of broken ribs.

Meanwhile, Beauty was still in action. She swam towards her neighing foal and guided it towards an island in the middle of the river where they found shelter among the rain-lashed Port Jackson bushes.

About an hour later, Rian fought through the rain to find his grandfather who had collapsed unconscious by the water's edge about 300 metres downstream. The boy rushed back to his parents, and the old man was taken home by bakkie. He was suffering from shock and damaged ribs, but was soon recovering in the warmth and comfort of the farmhouse.

The horses, though, were still missing. Bitterly cold, search parties of the family and farm workers trudged their way along both sides of the river. It was almost five long hours before they found the horses on the island. Accepting a halter now, Beauty was led to safety. The foal refused, hysterically, to go anywhere near the water a second time. So Rian and his brother Henti struggled through the rain, carrying the poor shivering creature to firm ground.

'Safe at last,' murmured Rian, as he pulled off his sodden clothes. His wellington boots were filled with water. 'Now, how about some breakfast?'

Later that year, Beauty was awarded a gold medal by the SPCA – the first horse to have received this annual award for animal bravery. But the story of this plucky horse wasn't over. She came to the rescue a second time. When the Palomino mare died after her foal was born, Beauty adopted this foal as her own. The little orphan suckled side by side with Sultan, and Beauty wouldn't let either of them wander away.

'Told you I chose well,' said Rian, with a grin.

## The Work of the SPCA

*The Society for the Prevention of Cruelty to Animals has many branches all over South Africa. Though prevention of cruelty to animals remains, sadly, one of their main activities, the promotion of love for animals is the thrust of their new awareness campaign. Horses, dogs and cats are among the animals they help regularly, as well as wild animals and birds. Supported almost entirely by voluntary contributions from the public, the SPCA would welcome your support too.*

# Lighthouse

Cape St Blaize stands high above the harbour of Mossel Bay. On its crest is a lighthouse, and the huge cave below is known as Bats Cave. One summer day late in 1990, officers from the oil supply ship *Voorspeler* happened to notice two men wandering along the road from the lighthouse. They were carrying a bedraggled black and white kitten which they had found in the cave. Deciding on the spur of the moment that *Voorspeler* needed a ship's cat, the officers bought the skinny kitten from the men for twenty rands and a case of beer. Bats Cave was hardly a suitable name, so they decided to name the small bundle of fur, Lighthouse.

That was how Lighthouse became an official member of the crew of *Voorspeler* and she was given the rank of Chief Ratcatcher. As on all ships of the Unicorn Line, crew members had to have special security clearance because they often worked in places of military importance. So the cat Lighthouse was duly issued with an identity card, complete with photograph and 'signature' (by pawprint).

Lighthouse quickly became used to life on board with the ten-man crew. She calmly selected a comfortable chair for herself in the captain's cabin, and after that it was unwise for any human to dare sit in her chair! Sharp claws would spring out to indicate her displeasure. She enjoyed her walks on the ship's bridge as well. The crew had to make special perspex covers to put over the emergency stop buttons. Lighthouse considered the control panel a part of her private walkway and more than once stopped the main engines by treading on a button.

The crew enjoyed her company and fed her bits of their home-made biltong. She accepted gracefully enough, but she definitely preferred fish. At night, when the powerful working lights were on, small fish

would be attracted by the light and would be caught in the little waves that swilled over the *Voorspeler's* low decks. Lighthouse would watch for these with glee - and then pounce! She took the fish back to a cabin floor and played with them there, batting them around from paw to paw, before she ate them. Sometimes she would even take a powerful-smelling fish to bed with her - which didn't make her too popular with the crew member whose bed she chose to share!

But Lighthouse had no favourites. She was quite happy just to curl up with whoever she chose at the time. Different crews came aboard. She accepted them all on what she considered was her ship. As cats do, she continued to remain quite independent. Not that human beings were not useful to her, she had to admit.

There was the time in Mossel Bay harbour when she used up one of the nine lives which cats are supposed to have. There is a heavy swell in the harbour and huge, empty tyres are hung on the quayside wall to protect ships as they heave to and fro. Lighthouse had been having a difference of opinion with a local tom-cat. He gave chase, she fled back to the ship, and lost her balance as the *Voorspeler* heaved. Four paws scrabbled at the wet metal deck. Then, with one pitiful mewing cry, Lighthouse was pitched overboard and fell helplessly into the harbour. Fortunately, one of the crew saw her go and leapt in to save her. A small, wet, drowning cat is not an easy object to find in dark, oily water. But he did find her - after a tiring hour - sheltering inside one of the tyres, and peering out from its gaping black rubber interior.

61

Whenever *Voorspeler* docked, Lighthouse would wander ashore. She always managed to be back in time for sailing, except for one rather memorable occasion. In March 1991, *Voorspeler* put in to Cape Town harbour for her two-yearly overhaul. Two years of strain and wear had to be put right in two weeks. The ship stood in the Robinson Dry Dock beside the Maritime Museum, and Lighthouse promptly went off to explore the excitements of the Waterfront. When repairs were completed, the water refilled the dry dock and *Voorspeler* moved to H berth in Duncan Dock. Then came an urgent message from the Unicorn Lines head office that they must be ready to sail at midnight. But Lighthouse was not on board. So, with a rather miserable crew, *Voorspeler* left without her ship's cat. Before they left, a despairing telex was sent to Unicorn Lines: 'Lighthouse missed ship.'

Berthed alongside was the great ocean-going tug *Wolraad Woltemade*. Several of her crew recognised Lighthouse when they saw an anxious black and white shape patrolling the quay. The captain managed to persuade her to come on board, but she spat angrily and hid if anyone tried to catch her. So a phone call was put through to *Voorspeler's* captain, who just happened to be on leave in Cape Town. He knew Lighthouse well but he wasn't sentimental about cats.

No coaxing and persuading. He just stood on the quay and shouted, 'Cat! Cat!' and Lighthouse came running to him, purring with pleasure.

More phone calls from the Unicorn Lines office established that *Voorspeler* was already in Mossel Bay, and due to sail again at 9pm. She was warned to wait for her missing crew member. Lighthouse was booked onto a Flitestar flight, rushed to DF Malan Airport in a cat basket and given V.I.P treatment in the pilot's cabin. The plane didn't touch down in George until 9.15pm but a hired car was waiting to whisk the missing crew member swiftly to her ship.

The next morning, Lighthouse was paraded in front of the captain, as any human crew member would be. She seemed unconcerned as she was fined one day's pay for missing ship. Then she was given an official Letter of Warning that if she repeated such misconduct, she risked being dismissed from Unicorn Lines employment. Lighthouse listened briefly to the captain's almost stern voice, and then busied herself with a morning wash behind the ears.

But her sailing days on the *Voorspeler* came to an end in March 1993 when the ship was sold to a French shipping line. The new French crew wanted to keep Lighthouse on board, but her many friends refused to hear of it. Lighthouse was transferred, quite

## Mossel Bay

*In Bats Cave, Cornelis de Houtman, a Dutch seaman who climbed in there 1595, found a pile of mussel shells. It was clear to him that these were the only food supplies of previous visitors and, apart from the shellfish, there didn't seem to be much to eat, so he named the place Mossel Bay. It was a poor place in his day, and only surged into modern prominence when oil was discovered off shore. Oil brought new life to the town with the huge Mossgas project in recent years, which has involved an enormous processing works on shore, a working oil rig off shore, and ships bringing supplies to both.*

happily along with many of the *Voorspeler* crew, to the tug *Voortrekker*, where she was allowed to proudly continue her sea voyaging.

Already known as the 'Reluctant Lady', the 11 000 ton *Voortrekker* had hit the headlines back in 1982 when she refused to be launched. She was a heavy anchor tug, designed to manoeuvre the oil rig's massive anchors and she stuck fast on the slipway. Eventually extra grease persuaded her to go out into the element for which she was built.

Lighthouse sailed on *Voortrekker* for a further six months until her cat's nine lives were finally used up. On 10 September 1993, *Voortrekker* tragically capsized in terribly heavy seas off Mossel Bay, although an air bubble kept her afloat. Three of the crew managed to swim to safety after being trapped inside for more than twelve hours, though one died shortly after. Rescuers towed the ship towards shallower water in the hope of being able to send divers to free those, including Lighthouse, who were still trapped inside. Sadly, off the Gourits River mouth, *Voortrekker* settled deeper and deeper into the mud, the cloudy water making it almost impossible for divers to see anything at all. Sadly, the *Voortrekker* sank there. No-one could do anything more. And so the sea career of the ship's cat, Lighthouse, was ended.

# Hunter's moon

Life was never dull with an otter in and around the house. The house Antony's parents had built near Gansbaai in the Cape was home to chickens, cats, visiting dassies and several cows (one of them blind but quite able to find her way around). But when Oswald the otter arrived – well, Antony was never certain what would happen next.

One night, his usually rather talkative father was quietly looking out of the window.

'It's a hunter's moon tonight,' he said thoughtfully.

Antony joined him and stared up at the sky. 'But there isn't any moon at all!'

'That's why it's ideal for hunters, Ant. Nights of no moon slip by darkly, on shadowed wings.'

'Sounds like poetry, Dad. Who wrote that?'

'Probably your mother,' admitted Dad, smiling to himself as he spoke. 'She's the real poet in this family. But you can see, Ant, how incredibly dark the bush is out there. That's where the jackal goes when he's slinking up on the farmer's lambs. He likes the dark. He's one of nature's cowards.'

'Remember that night last year when I came across a lynx?' replied Mom, joining them.

'What really happened, Mom?' asked Antony.

'It was the broody hen's fault, really,' said Mom. 'She was risking her life nesting out in a lonely part of the bush. I had persuaded her to move to what I thought was a safe home in the old oil drum. That night she was sitting on a batch of fifteen eggs and I went out to check on the progress. It was very dark. A hunter's moon, like tonight. I bent down slowly to look into the back of the old oil drum, and inside I saw two gleaming yellow eyes. The thing leapt out at me with a wild screech, only centimetres from my face. I nearly died of fright.'

'No wonder you screamed.'

'It was a beautiful creature. Quite a young one,' said Mom. 'It had long pointed ears and reddish fur – so soft. It was like a cat, but with a sharp, cruel face.'

'Rooikat, they call it round here,' said Dad. 'It's a member of the cat family.' And then he turned to Antony. 'Time you were in bed, young man.'

Towards morning, just as it was becoming light, Antony was woken by spine-chilling noises – shrieks and growls, screams, snarls and hisses. He could recognise some of the noises as Oswald's. But what were the others? Hens cackling in alarm, that was part of it. Antony was out of bed in a flash and he leapt through the window at record speed. From the stoep, one glance showed him the whole story.

'A lynx!' he shouted excitedly, in through the window. 'Oswald is chasing it!' And he pelted off, following the cries which were now heading far off into the distance.

He didn't get far. It was still too dark to find a way through the undergrowth. He listened, heard nothing more, and returned to the house picking thorns out of his bare feet.

'What happened?' demanded Dad who appeared beside him in his dressing gown, carrying his gun.

Antony was proud. 'I saw a lynx standing on the rocks there, under the hens' roost. Oswald was protecting them.'

'Good for Oswald! But he's not as fast as a lynx, that's for sure.'

And so peace returned once more to the house. The lights went out again and Antony snuggled down into his warm bed, though he found it difficult to go to sleep. He was half awake when Oswald returned. Antony heard him jump through the living room window and slip quietly into the bathroom.

The bathroom? Strange soft sounds made Antony decide he'd better take a look. He grabbed his bedside torch and went through the darkened living room. Oswald had pulled all the towels off the rails in the bathroom and was busy making himself a bed in the corner. Antony wondered if he should do anything. But Oswald was the night's hero, after all, and surely he deserved his comfort. He went back to bed.

The next morning Mom was awake before the others as usual. She put Oswald's morning piece of bread on the low table and gave him a call. No Oswald! Curious, she thought. As often as not he was up on his back legs, squeaking at the bread-tin. Then she did hear a faint squeak – from the bathroom.

There was Oswald, staggering out from under her new bath towel. One eye was closed and he had a terrible gash on his head. It had bled all over the towel, and his front legs were scratched and bleeding where the lynx had raked him.

'Oh, you poor thing!' breathed Mom.

Dad was standing beside her and they watched Oswald limp his way miserably to the kitchen, rather a sorry sight on his lacerated paws. But he did not seem unduly saddened, and by the time Antony joined them, he was acting the wounded hero while Mom carefully administered first aid.

For quite a few nights after that, Oswald refused to sleep in his old box outside under the leafy trees. His guardianship of the hens had obviously been tested to the absolute limit. At bedtime he made straight for the bathroom and showed clearly that he considered the bathroom his new sleeping quarters. Antony brought in the sacks Oswald usually slept on and arranged them in a corner.

News came from the farm next door of missing hens. The farmer set traps and caught two full-grown lynx. One was in very poor condition, with its legs badly mauled and scars all over its body.

'I suppose that's the one Oswald tackled,' was Antony's opinion. 'I knew he won.'

Oswald's own celebration came about a week later. He had been particularly frisky all evening. As a special treat, Mom had given him a whole bag of different sized marbles. He inspected the bag gleefully on the floor, feeling it all over. Then he lay back and passed the bag backwards and forwards from front paws to back. Finally he fiddled and poked with his fingers at the little plastic bag until – hurray! – the marbles spilled all over the floor. He threw them wildly round the room. The cat fled for its life.

Then Oswald decided he needed the marbles together again. He started searching. He lay on his back, groping under furniture, squeaking if human legs happened to be in the way. Having found most of them, he took his collection out into the hall.

Once more the marbles were hurled into the air, and they fell onto the tiled floor with a clatter. Antony was weak with laughter by this time. Mom had difficulty persuading Oswald to go to bed. He went in the end, but he wasn't pleased.

Antony went to the bathroom early the next morning – and stopped in the doorway, aghast. Oswald had wreaked havoc during the night.

Everything he could reach had been dragged down to the floor, either pulled under the bath or hauled into it. Towels were twisted round the waste pipe under the basin. Dad's dressing gown was in shreds. The pretty plastic curtains which Mom liked so much had been ripped from their rod, torn joyously and hurled into the tub like a bundle of old washing. The bath-mat had been chewed to pieces. Toothpaste was smeared all over the floor and toothbrushes were bare of all their bristles. The only thing he had left untouched was the soap.

In the bath, lay Oswald, with a satisfied smile on his face. That was the last time he slept in the bathroom!

## Otters in the Wild

*Oswald was a Cape clawless otter, and his colouring (as was usual with this species) was warm brown with a silvery shine on his head and shoulders. An otter can measure over a metre long, from its twitching, inquisitive nose to the tip of its strong tail. Each paw has five 'fingers', the back ones for better propulsion when swimming. Otters are liveliest at night and eat almost anything but they prefer fish, crabs and frogs. They make amusing, though often destructive, household pets as Morna Eyre and her family soon discovered. This chapter is only part of her original story. Otters in the wild are at the top of their particular food chain and so have few natural enemies other than pythons and crocodiles. Confident and powerful in the water, otters normally take their catch back to the burrow to eat later. The female looks after her litter of cubs alone, though male and female often hunt together.*

# Scotty Smith's horse and other diversions

On a Saturday morning in 1884, a handsome black stallion was being paraded round the auction ring. 'See for yourselves, gentlemen!' called Mr Goodchild, the auctioneer, persuasively. 'Try out this fine mount before you buy.'

Several possible buyers had already ridden thoughtfully around Kimberley's market square. The bidding was brisk that morning.

'Going...going...' Called Mr Goodchild, as yet another interested rider swung up onto the horse's back. There was a long pause, then horse and rider galloped off into the distance and out of sight of the astonished public and auctioneer. 'Gone!' he added, realising what had happened. 'To Scotty Smith.'

This typical story of the most famous rogue in South African history could have ended there. Some months later Scotty Smith walked into the auctioneer's office. Being told that Mr Goodchild was at the nearby hotel, Scotty went over to join him at the bar.

'That's the thief!' yelped Goodchild. 'Where's the horse you stole?'

'Careful,' advised Scotty, 'I've just paid for it at your office. Here's my receipt. Now, how about a drink?'

And while the auctioneer was gaping, Scotty turned to the hotel owner. 'Last time I was here I left in a bit of a hurry,' he said. 'Seems I forgot to pay my bill. Here's what I owe you.' He placed the money on the bar and smiled happily at everyone.

We shall never be sure which of the hundreds of stories about him are true. Scotty insisted that he came from a noble Scots family and that he had trained as a vet in Edinburgh. His full name, so he said, was George St Leger Gordon Lennox, and he loved horses so much that he could never resist the chance of stealing a good one.

George Brooke was driving a four-mule cart to Kimberley one day. He happened to pass an ox-wagon with an old man sitting, hunched over in it. The oxen were outspanned and grazing, but a horse was strangely enough tethered to the back of the cart.

'Why don't you let the horse graze too?' asked George.

The old man scowled. 'I'd like to,' he said, 'but I hear that Scotty Smith's around. He might steal it'.

George went on in to Kimberley, where he sold his butter and eggs and vegetables at the market. On the way home the next morning, near the Frankfurt Hotel, he passed the ox-wagon again, but saw no horse.

'It was stolen!' shrieked the old man. 'My only horse! I camped outside last night when I could have stayed at the hotel. I had the horse tied up and slept with a loaded gun beside me. It did no good. When I woke this morning, my precious horse was gone.'

He was giving George a whole string of uncomplimentary descriptions of Scotty Smith when a bearded man rode up leading the missing horse. 'I'm Scotty Smith,' said the newcomer. 'Be careful of what you say. I took your horse to teach you a lesson. I've never robbed a poor man yet.'

Instead of being grateful, the old man exploded with fury. 'If I'd seen you last night,' he screamed, 'I'd have shot you'.

'I thought as much,' chuckled Scotty. 'That's why I unloaded your gun before I took your horse'.

Although there are plenty of tales about Scotty stealing horses and keeping them, it seems he took heed of people's feelings too. Consider the case of the young officer saddled with the task of taking a hundred horses north to the British South Africa Police stationed in what was then called Rhodesia. He got as far as Mafeking, tied up the horses in the middle of the town, and booked into the hotel without bothering to post a sentry. The next morning there wasn't a horse in sight. For three days he and his troopers searched frantically. All had vanished. Knowing he could get court-marshalled and drummed out of the B.S.A.P., the young man went miserably to the bar to have a drink. Was it possible, he asked the barman, to hire some Baralong trackers? He was desperate. At this point a bearded stranger told him to pull himself together. He wasn't behaving like an officer at all. At dawn, the officer awoke to the sound of the neighing of many horses outside the hotel. All one hundred had mysteriously returned.

Horses were one way of travelling: stage coach was another. Alexander Gibson was driving a coach from De Aar to Kimberley with a fine team of twelve matched chestnut horses. One of his passengers was particularly complimentary about the horses and even took the reins for a while to try them out. When they reached Magersfontein, the horses were unhitched and replaced by a fresh team, while the weary passengers went to the local inn for some refreshment. Scotty (as you might have guessed it was) said he would continue to walk on ahead. 'Just pick me up along the road,' he told Alexander.

The coach started off, and Alexander looked out for his missing passenger, but although it was a bright, moonlit night, the mysterious passenger was nowhere to be seen. Alexander blew his horn and stopped a few times, before giving up and driving on. When he reached Kimberley, he was told that the entire chestnut team he had left behind had been stolen. The thief (and Alexander wasn't surprised at the news) was said to be Scotty Smith.

About three years later, Alexander was staying at the Vryburg Hotel and he recognised the passenger who had admired his horses. Alexander immediately walked straight up to him.

'You must be Scotty Smith,' he said.

'That's right,' admitted Scotty happily, 'and you're part owner of Gibson's Red Star Coaches'.

'So, what about our chestnut team?'

'Tell you what,' said Scotty, 'I'm living an honest life now. I'm farming and doing quite well. Trust me and don't start making a fuss, and I'll see you don't lose out. Here's my hand on it.'

Not knowing why he should think of even trusting the rogue, Alexander Gibson merely nodded and gingerly held out his hand.

The next day, a young Bushman led fourteen horses into the Gibson stables, and handed them over, together with a saddle, a bridle and a letter.

'Dear Gibson,' read the letter, 'I hope this will square our account. The extra animals, saddle and bridle will make up for the fact that these horses are not as good as those I borrowed from you. If you can give this lad a job, I shall be obliged. He works hard, but he can't be cured of cattle stealing. If he cannot steal anybody else's cattle, he usually takes mine.'

From Scotty Smith, South Africa's own 'Robin Hood', that was rich humour indeed!

### Saving a General

*During the First World War, General Louis Botha, the first Prime Minister of the Union of South Africa, led the attack on German South West Africa or Namibia as it is known today. Scotty served his adopted country as desert scout. Knowing that Botha had a habit of going far ahead of the main column of troops, Scotty formed his own private bodyguard. When, as expected, a German desert patrol arrived intending to ambush the general and capture him, they found themselves ambushed instead. General Botha only discovered afterward what Scotty had done.*

# The military menace

They have given me the name 'Joey'; I'm not sure why. My proper family name is *Struthio camelus*, which is more dignified. Of course, ostriches aren't related to camels! But we have sometimes been called the 'camel bird' because we have similar skills. Like camels, we can cross sandy deserts on our broad-spreading feet and go for months without water. Israelite kings and Roman emperors knew of the splendour of our plumes, and the ostrich feather was a symbol of justice to the ancient Egyptians.

Before I tell you about my sentry duty service with No.1 South African Infantry Battalion at Bloemfontein, I think you should know something about my chickhood – or childhood, as you would say.

I was hatched on one of the more gracious farms near Oudtshoorn some time around 1950. I pecked my way out of my egg to see a suitably ornate palace, red-roofed with carved stone turrets. It seemed most suitable for a bird of my breeding. But I soon learned that this fine house was only for the human farmer to live in – and not for me. He fed me well, I have to admit, on the best lucerne with mealies and greens. He used to add some tasty chopped bones and bits of eggshell for the calcium needed to strengthen my already rather impressive legs.

I was not really all that keen on having any visitors. At first I would hide when they came – crouching down low so that my mottled yellow and brown plumage blended excellently with the dry grass and scrub. Then, when my first grey feathers appeared, I learned how to lie almost completely flat along the ground, as if I were a rock. I did not 'bury my head in the sand' as some of you seem to think. Ostriches are not that stupid! I just stayed perfectly still.

I was about 18 months old, beginning to show off my first mature feathers, when the thunderstorm came. Of course, I had heard thunder before as it growled away over the Little Karoo. But rain was rare in those parts and storms even rarer. So the clap of thunder and the flash of lightning came as quite a shock.

What I didn't expect was the effect it would have on my parents. My father inflated his neck like a cobra and started to roar like a lion. My mother, however, flapped her grey wings for the last time and died on the spot. That in itself I could have accepted. After all, birds do die. But I can hardly bear to tell you about what followed. Two humans, wearing white coats, arrived to drag my mother's body away. They put it on the back of a bakkie and took it to a long shed on the farm. Driving through the rain storm, they neglected to close all the gates behind them. I followed and peered in through the window.

No – I am not going to describe what I saw. Instead, I will remind you of the facts and the figures of our noble breed, as humans see us. 'Nothing is wasted.' Humans eat the meat as ostrich steaks, they dry it as biltong, they use the hide for handbags and purses, they grease guns and boots with ostrich fat, and they grind bones into fertiliser. And our fine feathers are turned into colourful fans, plumes, trimmings, artificial flowers and even dusters.

From that day on, I lost all trust in the human race. What is more, I waged a ceaseless war against any person dressed in white. At the tourist end of the farm, they soon discovered that I was not going to co-operate with their ostrich races – still less allow fat visitors to pose for photographs on my back. After I had dumped one schoolboy in the feeding trough and chased his father back to the bus, I was not required for such activities again.

Instead, I was sold (though none of the money came to me) to a Free State farmer who was looking for what he called 'an aggressive bird'. My habit of chasing any wandering human was apparently exactly what was needed. His farm had long straight fences, so I was able to stretch my legs and keep training by running alongside the cars which drove on the far side. Sixty-two kilometres per hour was my top speed, so they told me, and I reached that speed from a standing start after only a few seconds. Their cars have very poor acceleration compared to me!

But my legs are not only for running. I kick – forwards and very fast. There was one nasty occasion when a man climbed in to my field in the early morning. I was busy at the time, sorting out a few choice beetles and gulping some good grit for extra flavour. This man was trying to steal a sheep, but it really didn't matter to me *what* he was doing. He wore a white shirt, and he was trespassing on my territory. I kicked him hard and that seemed to be enough. Had I wished to make better use of the sharp main toe on my foot, I could have split him in two.

Things got a bit unpleasant after that. One man came at me and viciously pushed a bunch of thorns into my face so I that had to quickly shut my eyes. Then another man pulled some sort of sack over my head. I was herded into a truck like common cattle and taken for a long ride.

When I was allowed to see again, I was in Bloemfontein, doing my military service! With an elite corps: the Mechanised Leader Wing, where the junior lieutenants were trained. I was put in charge of the perimeter fence. This was exactly what I enjoyed doing most. Once, I indicated firmly to the young chefs that I did not approve of their white costumes, and lunch that day was served rather late, but I think my preference was clearly established.

Watching the troopies training and exercising was actually rather amusing, but what I liked best was joining them on a long run.

Unfortunately, our unit was moved to become part of 1 South African Infantry Battalion, so I had to teach the new lot what I liked and disliked. One of my encounters was with the army chaplain, who leads the church services for the troops. He was trotting off on his early morning jog, wearing only white shorts and a T-shirt. After I chased him into the battalion headquarters, they had a lot more respect for me.

Added respect came from my attendance record at sports parades. The humans do a weekly 2,4 kilometre time trial. I join in – taking time off for eating thorns, swallowing stones and pulling up tufts of grass. I swallowed a cool drink bottle once. I don't recommend you try it.

Some of my temper came from living alone – apart from the humans. Who can blame a beautiful bird like myself being sensitive with never a friend in sight? Still, it cheered me up to hear the commanding officer refer to me as 'Head of Security Affairs'. But, I'm still worried about thunderstorms. Gunfire, I don't mind. Thunder, I do. It could be the death of me yet.

## Feather Palaces

*The details of Joey the Ostrich serving with the military at Bloemfontein are true, though we made a few guesses about his earlier life. He died in 1989 – after an unusually powerful thunderstorm. Ostriches brought huge fortunes to their owners in the 1880s when ostrich feathers were the height of ladies' fashion. After the Second Anglo-Boer War, the boom flourished again. By 1910, ostrich feathers were bringing over two million pounds a year to the ostrich farmers in South Africa. Many farmers built themselves enormous, luxury houses which are still known as 'feather palaces'. When cars were invented, passengers wanted neater, tight-fitting styles, such as the cloche so wide hats and flamboyant feathers went out of fashion. The days of the ostrich feather had gone forever.*

# The great tusker

He was known as Mafunyane, which means 'the irritable one', though for a long time nobody knew why this impressive elephant had such a bad temper. Mafunyane lived in the Kruger National Park, and was one of the great tuskers nicknamed The Magnificent Seven. His own pair of tusks was often judged the most beautiful of them all: perfectly matched, they were so heavy that he had to raise his massive head constantly to keep them clear of the ground. When he was tired and lowered his head, the tips of the tusks polished themselves to razor-sharp points on the sand as he walked.

To keep a careful watch on such fine elephant bulls, it was necessary to put a reasonably tight-fitting collar round their necks with a radio device on it which would beep out continuous signals. Listening to these signals, the rangers would be able to easily follow the movements of each tusker, without having to search the bush constantly in order to find out where they had disappeared to. If the signal kept coming repeatedly from the same place, it was very likely that the elephant was either quite sick or dead – or that it had torn off its radio collar, as one bull, João, did again and again.

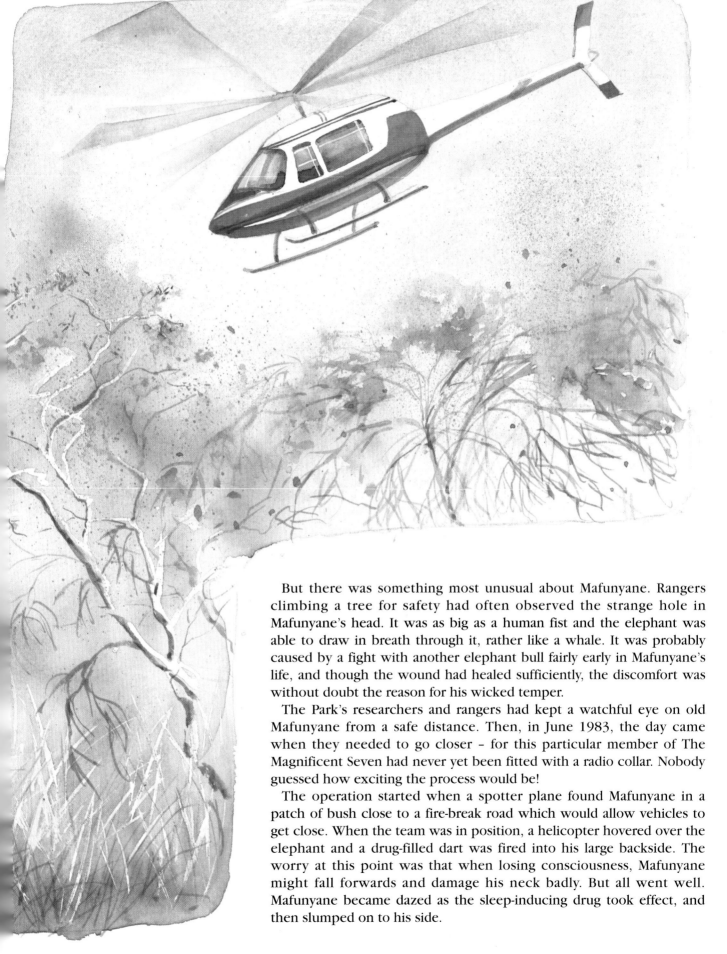

But there was something most unusual about Mafunyane. Rangers climbing a tree for safety had often observed the strange hole in Mafunyane's head. It was as big as a human fist and the elephant was able to draw in breath through it, rather like a whale. It was probably caused by a fight with another elephant bull fairly early in Mafunyane's life, and though the wound had healed sufficiently, the discomfort was without doubt the reason for his wicked temper.

The Park's researchers and rangers had kept a watchful eye on old Mafunyane from a safe distance. Then, in June 1983, the day came when they needed to go closer – for this particular member of The Magnificent Seven had never yet been fitted with a radio collar. Nobody guessed how exciting the process would be!

The operation started when a spotter plane found Mafunyane in a patch of bush close to a fire-break road which would allow vehicles to get close. When the team was in position, a helicopter hovered over the elephant and a drug-filled dart was fired into his large backside. The worry at this point was that when losing consciousness, Mafunyane might fall forwards and damage his neck badly. But all went well. Mafunyane became dazed as the sleep-inducing drug took effect, and then slumped on to his side.

The National Park staff moved into action swiftly. While some made plaster casts of his wondrous tusks (in case they were ever lost or stolen by poachers), others checked his teeth (to estimate his age) and measured his huge body. All the time, more staff kept a check on the elephant's heartbeat and breathing. Nobody wanted him to wake up too soon! The radio collar was fastened on quite securely. Then a dose of antidote to the original drug was injected, and everybody stood well clear.

One large, leathery ear flapped – a common sign that the elephant was about to get up. But this, for Mafunyane, was not easy. He was still groggy from the drug, and his tusks were very heavy. He rocked the great barrel of his body and try to get his legs under him to lever himself upward, but it didn't work. The

rangers rushed forward and heaved against his shoulder and head as he tried again and again. But each attempt was weaker than the one before.

As the old elephant's head dropped, the human team quickly tied a loop round him, threw the rope over the branch of a high tree and fastened the end to a four-wheel-drive vehicle. As the vehicle was driven forward, the rope tightened and the wheels spun furiously. Everyone available pushed and pulled at Mafunyane's body. It was no use. He was too tired and too drugged to stand.

Hurried consultations, then an urgent message was sent by radio. While the rangers waited, they sprayed water on Mafunyane's body to keep him cool. Before long a powerful front-end loader arrived and, after more discussion, the driver started to push a pile of earth against Mafunyane's back. To prevent dirt getting into his breathing hole, they draped a canvas tarpaulin over the elephant.

The earth which had been heaped against Mafunyane's body certainly helped. The tusker seemed to understand what was being done, and shifted his weight more comfortably as each load was put in place. But the steel scoop of the front-end loader was hardly a gentle piece of machinery with which to help the elephant, so the driver fastened some planks over them. Then he drove the machine forward and 'scooped up' the elephant as he did so.

The result was dramatic! With his feet firmly on the ground at last, Mafunyane decided it was time to live up to his nickname, 'the irritable one', once again. He swung towards the front-end loader, which had been pushing him around, and charged. The driver abandoned his vehicle and fled. What Mafunyane would have done to the machine nobody knows, for at that moment the helicopter took off. The clattering roar of the rotor blades enraged Mafunyane even more and the swirl of wind sent the tarpaulin flapping around the elephant's head.

Since the loader had stopped moving, Mafunyane presumably decided it was dead or at any rate defeated, so he turned his attention to his new canvas enemy. That gave him considerable satisfaction. His great tusks tore through the tarpaulin most enjoyably and his huge feet pounded what was left into the dust.

Meanwhile, all the game park staff had retreated at high speed – some in vehicles, but most on foot. It was good to see 'the irritable one' back to health and strength, though not so good to remain within range. But Mafunyane left them in peace. Honour was satisfied!

During the weeks that followed, the signals from the radio collar round Mafunyane's neck showed that he was covering his usual long distances as he browsed and fed each day. So there were no worries about his health until November that year. The signal had been coming from the same spot for a week. Two of the game park staff drove out into the far northwest area of the Kruger National Park to investigate. Sure enough, the radio collar was there – what was left of it. Only hovering vultures gave a clue to where Mafunyane himself could be found. His imposing skull lay white in the sun, and the remains of bones had been stripped and scattered far by hyenas. His tremendous tusks were found and are now on display in the elephant museum at the Park's Letaba camp.

Though death is always sad, one consolation is that he died a natural death, and wasn't murdered by poachers as has been the fate of so many elephants.

## The Magnificent Seven

*About fifteen years ago, the game rangers in the Kruger National Park named seven of the great tuskers 'The Magnificent Seven'. Each had its own different character and a magnificent pair of tusks. The longest (measuring 3,17 metres and 3,06 metres) belonged to Shawu, named after an area near Shingwedzi. Then there was João, probably named after the Portuguese pioneer settler João Albasini; Ndlulamithi, meaning 'taller than the trees'; Kambaku, 'the big elephant'; Mafunyane, 'the irritable one'; Dzombo, named after a local river; and Shingwedzi, the name of a rest camp and a river. Six have now died or been shot by poachers, though the fate of João is unknown. He was last seen in 1985, and may still be alive somewhere in the Kruger National Park.*

# Andrea in action

Beside the road were two cardboard boxes. Something about them looked suspicious, so Constable Ivan Kotze slowed down and stopped. He had been driving along Church Street in Pretoria, on his way out to the South African Police Dog School. So it was highly appropriate that he should be the one to investigate the shoe boxes – for each one contained a wriggling, black and white border collie puppy. Ivan took them through to the Dog School, where they were named Andrea and Louise. He already had a dog of his own to work with, so he lost track of the two puppies.

Like all border collies, the pups were trained initially to work as sheepdogs. But not all of the dogs are able to meet the incredibly high standards which are understandably required by the police, and those who do not are put on a list to be sold if possible. This is what happened to Andrea, who had been moved to the Police Dog Unit in Cape Town. But then another strange coincidence occurred.

Ivan Kotze had also been transferred to Cape Town. His own specially-trained sniffer dog was sick; he had been told to look for another, and he was feeling generally down-hearted. Walking past one of the many lines of kennels, he tripped and almost fell. Suddenly, yelping and licking at him through the wire mesh, was a friendly black and white face! It was Andrea and she recognised him. So Ivan decided Andrea must become his next dog. She was put on to sniffer dog training and proved highly skilful.

When classes of schoolchildren lined up outside the fenced-off enclosure to see the police dogs go through part of their normal training, Andrea was part of the display. A little cloth bag containing dagga would be hidden by a policeman in the pocket of one pupil, and Andrea was encouraged to go sniffing. It was a great game! The children squealed with excitement as the dog sniffed around them, and Andrea was rewarded with a warm 'That's good!' from her handler when she found the bag – and she always did.

Those were the fun times. Most of her time was spent working, though she enjoyed that too. She lived in a concrete pen - which looked a bit bleak to the visiting children, but was fine for Andrea. She was kept fit and healthy. Her daily meal consisted of dog biscuits with a thick bone twice a week to act as her toothbrush. She gulped down her regular spoonful of sunflower oil which kept her coat shining.

By this time, Ivan had been promoted to Captain. As an officer, he did not have an individual dog allocated to him any longer, so Andrea was taken over by Anton van Niekerk. He continued her training, teaching her the basic commands of Sit! and Heel! and Wait! just like any normal dog. Then came the more active training of crossing bridges, jumping fences, swimming across pools and hurrying through storm-water drains. Andrea developed her own technique for tunnels like that. While Anton hurried round to the far end of the tunnel, she lay down inside and took a quick rest!

The bond of trust between dog and handler grew steadily. So Anton was thrilled when he was given permission to keep Andrea in the backyard at home. She loved it too, for though she was certainly never treated as a 'pet', the home setting made her feel extra special. When she had performed particularly well during the day, Anton did not feed her extra bits of food. That would have made her fat and less efficient. Instead, he rewarded her with the warmth of his voice - though just occasionally a tiny snippet of biltong might drop down near Andrea's quivering nose. By mistake, of course!

Each day, various police experts tested the dogs on different skills. Though all the border collies were being trained as sheepdogs, some would prove better at different things. Andrea was quick at finding the hidden bag of dagga and so drug detection became her special skill.

Perhaps she wondered why Anton was unable to do the same. Nobody had explained to her that a dog's power of scent is 250 000 times stronger than a human being's!

Each time that Anton sat outside his back door giving his boots an extra polish, Andrea knew that she was to go into action soon. Her ears pricked up and her tail wagged excitedly. Work, for her, was fun.

Then came the terrible morning when Anton woke up, called Andrea as he opened his kitchen door – and heard no answering yelp. The pen in the yard was empty. Somebody had climbed in and stolen her during the night. How it had been done baffled Anton completely, for Andrea would not have gone willingly unless she was drugged or half-unconscious. But more important was how to get her back.

Anton knew that police dogs sometimes died in the course of duty, but he wasn't prepared for his own special dog to vanish quite so suddenly. He had copies made of Andrea's photograph. He gave them to reporters and put the photos up in local shops asking for information. He had to admit to himself that he wasn't all that hopeful of ever getting her back. A well-trained dog like Andrea could fetch a really good

price for her thief. The newspapers carried the story and Radio Good Hope broadcast Anton's appeal. But sadly, nothing happened.

Then one day a schoolgirl cycled home to Kraaifontein and found a tired, dirty sheepdog lying asleep on her front stoep. She remembered hearing about a missing dog on the radio, and had seen Andrea's picture at the corner café. Bursting with excitement, she phoned the police. So Andrea returned home, thrilled to be back but unable to explain to Anton where she had been taken or how she had managed to escape.

Reunited, Andrea and Anton went back to work. A tip-off had been received that a large haul of dagga was on its way by rail to Cape Town. Andrea was one of the dogs chosen to sniff it out. Sealed containers sometimes arrived by ship or by rail, labelled 'clothes' or 'TV sets' to await collection. Some sixth sense warned the Customs Department or the Narcotics Bureau that a particular container might not contain what its label claimed. Perhaps the total weight was more or less than it should be. Or perhaps a sniffer dog had been put into action.

One container was sitting in the railway yard at Philippi. Andrea and another sniffer dog were taken there and at once Andrea became excited, yelping and running back to Anton to call his attention to what she had found. Her companion dog barked wildly too. The police duly put a team in hiding and waited.

At 9 am on 6 July 1992, a gang of men arrived to open the container. The police sprang from their hiding places and closed in – shots were fired – men shouted and ran – and seven were arrested. When the police examined the inside of the container, they found sacks containing nearly five million rands' worth of dagga. It was the largest haul of illicit dagga ever captured in the Western Cape. Those responsible had tried to confuse sniffer dogs by packing strong-smelling mothballs around the drug-filled sacks. But it took more than mothballs to fool Andrea!

There were congratulations all round, with cameras clicking and reporters swarming to catch the story. Andrea posed for the photographer with her tongue lolling out in happiness. Why was everybody so excited? This was just part of her working day.

## A Dog's Prayer

*O Lord of Humans,*

*make my master faithful to his fellowmen*

*as I am to him.*

*Give him a face as cheerful as my wagging tail;*

*and a spirit of gratitude like my licking tongue.*

*Fill him with my watchfulness, my courage,*

*and my readiness to sacrifice comfort or life.*

*Make him as good a man as I am a dog;*

*and make him worthy of me, his dog.*

### South African Police Dog Unit

*There is only one police dog training school in South Africa where all police dogs receive their special training, and that is the South African Police Dog School which is in Pretoria. Andrea actually works at the General Hennie de Witt complex in Cape Town. With 148 kennels, this is one of the largest working dog units in the world. Police training teams from other countries of the world often come to South Africa in order to pick up tips on the training of the various dogs which are used by the South African Police. Andrea is a real dog and her involvement in the record dagga haul is quite accurate, but some of the details of her training and her handler have been taken from other true accounts of police sniffer dogs.*

# The strangers

It was evening when we first noticed them. The sun was nearing the rim of the mountains, and we were camping that night in a green wood which spread across a valley with many gurgling streams. I was playing with my brother, chasing him through the trees, when he suddenly stopped and pointed. We could see them quite clearly: dark figures on the horizon against the setting sun.

Faintly, we heard their unusual barking sounds echoing among the rocks. A moment of excitement – something strange to look at – before it was time to sleep. But I wondered about them when I woke in the grey light before dawn. Were they dangerous? What happened if you went too close?

That morning, Oupa chose to take us all exploring. It was an early morning walk. 'There's more to find in the early morning,' he used to say. I was cold and only half awake. The breeze was nippy. I kept stumbling over the rocks, not being careful enough where I put my feet. So when we climbed round the rock-piled corner and found them right there in front of us, I was taken by surprise.

There were three of them, much bigger than I expected, and one of them was already awake and watching us, without much trust in his eyes. My brother and I sat on a rock ledge in the dawn sunlight, at a safe distance, and watched him too. I had been warned about these creatures often enough – but I was still fascinated. They seemed to move the same way we do, but they behaved in such curious ways. This one balanced on his hind legs and was covered in blue fur, though he had bare hands and a face rather like ours. The other two creatures were still asleep, wrapped up like large grubs, one grass-colour and one red. The upright one was chattering and pointing at us. This woke the sleeping ones, who sat up, climbed out of their soft cocoons, and left the skins crumpled on the ground.

That really frightened me. It was all too strange. I ran back to where Oupa was sitting, higher up on the hill. He seemed a bit bored by it all. He just sat there, enjoying the growing warmth of the sun, and chewing on a twig. He'd seen these creatures before.

'Keep away from them and they'll keep away from you,' was his advice. 'Whatever you do, don't try feeding them, or taking what they are eating. Then they become angry and dangerous.'

Oupa liked to sit and give wise advice. He could go on like that for hours if he had the chance. So when Mother came up, looking for my sister, I slipped away. I climbed out of sight behind a yellowwood tree, and made my way back towards our visitors in the valley. My brother soon joined me. He always copies what I do. For a while we played 'Grandmother's Footsteps' with them. The two of us would move forward, so slowly that the strange creatures didn't notice. If they turned their backs, we jumped onto the next stone. When they turned round towards us again, we stayed very still. Sometimes they would think we were too close, and then they would bound towards us and wave their long arms. That meant we had to run back out of sight and begin again.

I was particularly interested by one of them with blue and white fur and smooth pink legs. He was bending over a pile of twigs and doing something which I couldn't see. Suddenly there was smoke, and then

yellow flames. I jumped back and hid behind a spreading protea bush. Here was something else which I didn't understand, and I knew it was dangerous. What surprised me was that the blue and white creature wasn't frightened at all. He stayed beside the hot smoke, coughing a bit while he arranged shining things in the fire. I watched as the flames grew less and the red heat glowed. This was fun. The dark blue creature walked up holding something else, round and black, which smelt sweet and delicious.

My mouth was watering. Where was my brother? He'd run away at the sight of the flame! Ignoring what Oupa had told me, I clambered round behind the brown ridge of rock which overlooks the slope and hauled myself up an old grey pine, which leaned across where the creatures were. From this vantage point, I could see right down into the round black thing. I don't know what I expected to see, but the dark brown liquid was definitely disappointing. I swung down from the splintered top branch on to a lower one, and I was just bending down to take hold of the next branch when the smoke circled round and attacked me. I couldn't see. My eyes smarted and

burned. Nasty, choking smoke. I reached up wildly, grabbed the wrong branch, and toppled over. Screeching, I hung by my feet. Of course, I could have grabbed onto the main trunk quite easily, but the next moment the dry branch suddenly cracked and snapped off. As I fell rapidly through the air, all I could catch was a handful of leaves.

I don't remember what happened next. I suppose I must have hit my head hard on a rock and been dazed. The dark blue creature must have captured me and wrapped me in something pink and flower-coloured. It was soft and hairy. I bit it but there was no taste. The creature was holding me firmly and I squeaked with fright.

The other creatures gathered round. They had strange, smooth pink faces, pointed noses and tiny teeth. One of them even made a cooing noise like Mother does. The others were a bit nervous. But how on earth could they possibly be nervous of me? They were all so much bigger than I was. I wriggled and wriggled, trying to get free, but the dark blue one held me tight. My head hurt. I put my hand up and it came away red. I whimpered.

The cooing creature brought out a shining object which oozed with wet liquid. The dark blue creature covered my nose and mouth with the flower–pink stuff and the next thing I felt was a moist calming feeling on my head, which was rather like cool mud. It smelt scented, like buchu and young buds.

Then they were carrying me away from the smoke and flame, towards where the rest of my family were chattering away, and not knowing what to do. Just like Oupa! All talk and retreating! Gently, I was put on a round-topped rock and the pink thing was folded away. I sat there, looking sharply around, not sure what would happen next. Nothing did. They stood still, apart from the blue and white one who was holding a black thing in front of his face. It had one round eye which stared at me. Then it clicked.

That was it! I'd had enough. I scampered off as fast as hands and feet could take me, straight up the cliff and back to Mother. Up on to her back where I clung as I used to when I was even smaller. Off we went, through the trees and bushes, all of us. Mother wasn't very kind later when she licked off that smelly stuff from the cut on my head.

I wanted to take one last look at the creatures. After all, they had been kind to me. But Mother was firm. 'No,' she said. 'That's quite enough excitement for a small baboon for one day.'

## Baboons in the Wild

*This is a true story, even if it is told from an unusual point of view. I was the 'dark blue creature' myself, camping with two others deep in the Cape mountains. The baboons came close to us, inquisitive, and a branch did break! Because they were wild baboons, wary of us, we were quite safe. The same is not true of the baboons you may encounter by the roads or in game parks. They have become used to human beings and will deliberately come close and grab at food or belongings. An adult male can weigh over 40 kilograms, and when standing upright can be a metre tall with long, sharp teeth. Don't ever offer baboons food! And keep your car windows closed.*

# The springbok horde

One morning Gert van der Merwe's wagon was plodding along the dry, hard bed of the Molope River when he noticed that his Bushman *touleier* seemed worried about something. Suddenly, the man left the oxen and ran off on to the high northern bank of the river bed and pressed his ear to the ground. It was near noon, so Gert stopped the wagon for a midday meal and rest. He was getting used to the sometimes unexplainable behaviour of the Bushmen. There was nothing in sight to be worried about. His wife had already started cooking when the Bushman raced back into the camp.

'The trekbokke are coming!' he told them urgently. 'Inspan the oxen. We must leave at once. It will be death to stay here.'

Gert looked around and could see nothing dangerous. But, for the sake of his family, he allowed the Bushman to lead the wagon away from the river bed and as far up a small hill as the oxen would pull it.

Gert had left the Transvaal in the 1870s when he was only ten. His family was part of the first Thirstland Trek. They spent their lives moving on and on with their sheep and cattle in search of grass. When the old people died, son Gert went on with the only life he knew – trekking sometimes in the Kalahari, often in the dry North West Cape. By the time he was twenty-one, he had a wife and three children, two cattle herders and a skilled Bushman tracker to lead the way from one water hole to the next.

It was this Bushman who led Gert to the top of the hill and pointed.

Gert saw a cloud of dust along the horizon. It was far away and didn't suggest any great danger. But, the Bushman persuaded him to pile thorn bushes as a barrier around the wagon. By now the dust was only a few miles away, For the first time, Gert felt a little nervous. He ordered his family to take shelter in the wagon and he tied up the dogs underneath.

The buck were still hidden in the dust, but hares and jackals and other small animals were now racing past the hill. Snakes were out in the open, too, moving fast. Gert and his men threw stones at the snakes but they seemed more concerned with a greater fear than flying pebbles.

At last, a distant drumming of hooves came on the dry air. The cloud of dust was dense and enormous, and the front rank of the springbok, running faster than galloping horses, could be seen. They were in such huge numbers that Gert found the sight quite frightening. He could see a front line of buck at least five kilometres long, but he could not guess how deep they were spread. Ahead of the main body were swift *voorlopers*, moving along as though they were leading an army into battle.

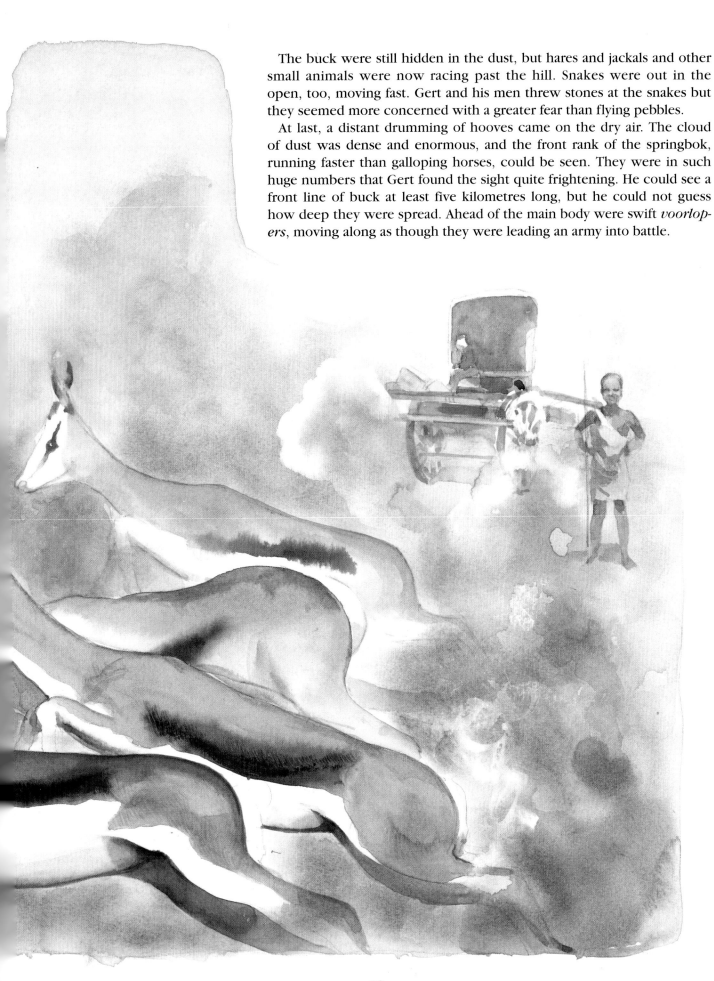

89

When the buck came within a kilometre of the hill, the Bushman ran to the wagon and climbed in. Gert and his herdsmen stayed with the cattle, which had sensed the danger and were milling around, lowing nervously. Gert's wife begged him to come inside the wagon, but he was excited by the spectacle and climbed onto the wagon seat for a better view.

The first solid wave of buck swept past on both sides of the hill. After that, they came continuously, making for the river and the open country beyond. As the number of animals became more and more, the groups of buck were crowded tighter and tighter. They could no longer swerve aside when they reached the thorns and the wagon. Some crashed into the wagon and were jammed in amongst the wheels, injured and trampled upon. The wagon became the centre of a horrific mass of dead and dying buck. By now the thorn barrier had been broken, and before long, the terrified, bellowing cattle stampeded and vanished into the thick cloud of rising dust. Gert had to let them go. There was only death for anyone who was silly enough to venture after them among the horns and hooves of the buck.

At the height of the rush the noise was overwhelming. Countless hooves powdered the dry surface to a fine dust. It soon became difficult to breathe. Gert's wife had to draw the blankets over herself and the children because the dust was beginning to smother them. Everything in the wagon was several centimetres deep in pale yellow dust.

Within an hour, the main body of springbok had passed, but that was not the end. Until long after sunset, hundreds of stragglers followed the great herd. Some were exhausted, some crippled, some bleeding. Gert wondered what had happened to the hares and jackals, and the snakes which had not taken cover in time. The next day he found the answer.

All night, lone buck passed the wagon. The air cleared, but dust rose again when there was any movement in the camp. At daybreak Gert climbed the hill to see whether he could find his cattle. He had food, and there was a water-hole not far away in the dry river bed, but without the oxen he was stranded.

The morning air was so clear, the day so bright, that Gert felt for a moment as though the events of the previous day had been little more than a nightmare.

90

Then he saw that the thorn trees which had covered the countryside, green with food for his cattle, were gaunt stumps and bare branches. The buck had brushed off all foliage as they rushed past, and splintered the young trees so that they wouldn't grow again.

Far in the distance Gert thought he could see a few of his oxen. After breakfast he set off with his men to recover them. Every donga leading into the river, every little gully was filled with dead buck. It seemed that the first buck had paused on the edge, considering leaping across, and before they could decide, the ruthless mass was upon them. Buck after buck was pushed into the donga, until the hollow was filled and the irresistible horde trampled over the bodies.

Small animals were lying dead everywhere – tortoises crushed almost to pulp, fragments of fur that had been hares. A tree, pointing in the direction of the advancing buck, had become a deadly spike on which two springbok were impaled.

For two weeks Gert camped on that hill beside the Molope, searching for his cattle. He found half of them. The fate of the others remained a mystery. Gert harnessed the survivors thankfully and the wagon containing his family rolled on, away from the scene of destruction. When in later years he told the tale to others, it was clear that it was the most memorable episode of his life. And he was glad to be alive.

## Leaps and Bounds

*The days when hundreds of thousands of springbok went on such mass migrations have passed, but the animal for so long adopted by our sporting teams is in no danger of extinction. The only gazelle found south of the Zambezi, springbok still gather in herds and trek periodically across the veld. When frightened, they bound into the air in leaps more than two metres high. Their horns curve outwards; their backs are reddish brown, with pure white underparts. The first rugby team to call themselves Springboks toured Britain in 1906. Gradually, in the years that followed, the players of other sports representing South Africa internationally called themselves Springboks too.*

# Eagle-eyes

The martial eagle circled high in the sky, waiting for the helicopter to land. The largest eagle in Africa, dark plumage on its head and wings, and a grey-white speckled underbody, he had learned to be wary of this huge, swirling, vibrating metal bird. But he knew that when it landed, other creatures were wary as well. In fact, they fled in all directions from that circle of whirring noise and blowing leaves. The huge man-made machine actually helped such predators as eagles with their hunting. As the small animals ran from the helicopter's landing, so the eagle would begin his dive. When he struck, in a whir of wings and talons, life was swiftly over for his chosen prey. There was enough power in his claws to crush the skull of a buck or a monkey.

On this particular day, a light southerly wind was blowing over the Kruger National Park and the descent of the game-watching helicopter sent clouds of dust and dry grass sweeping around the thorn trees. Terrified by the noise, a hare with his ears pressed flat against his skull, shot out of his shelter and streaked away. The eagle folded his wings and started to dive, so straight that he only just missed the swinging metal blades of the helicopter.

Perhaps it was the wind strengthened by the air currents made by the helicopter which caused the eagle to miscalculate. Or it might have been the sheer speed of the hare. Anyway, his outstretched talons hit the ground about a metre behind the running hare with such force that sand billowed out in a red cloud.

The force of the landing made the eagle skid wildly across the ground, beating desperately with his wings to stop himself rolling over. Eventually he brought his forced landing under control and sat with his wings drooping and beak snarling wide, as if blaming the helicopter for his failure.

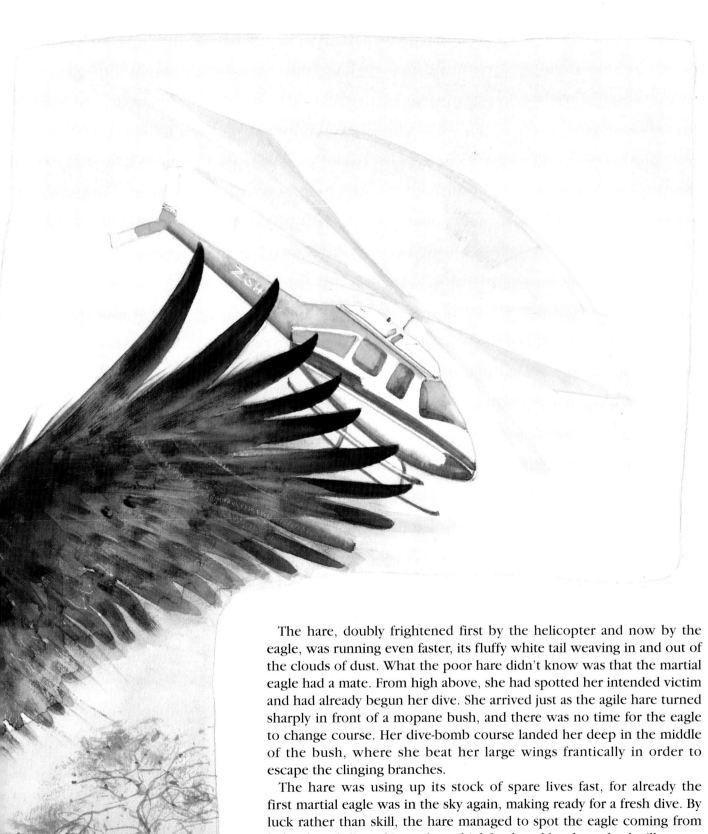

The hare, doubly frightened first by the helicopter and now by the eagle, was running even faster, its fluffy white tail weaving in and out of the clouds of dust. What the poor hare didn't know was that the martial eagle had a mate. From high above, she had spotted her intended victim and had already begun her dive. She arrived just as the agile hare turned sharply in front of a mopane bush, and there was no time for the eagle to change course. Her dive-bomb course landed her deep in the middle of the bush, where she beat her large wings frantically in order to escape the clinging branches.

The hare was using up its stock of spare lives fast, for already the first martial eagle was in the sky again, making ready for a fresh dive. By luck rather than skill, the hare managed to spot the eagle coming from behind, and slipped in under a thick bush and lay there dead still.

Angry and hungry, the eagle dived at the bush, his talons reaching out like daggers. But the twigs presented a brief barrier, giving the hunted hare a swift moment in which to shoot out from the shelter of the bush and race away across the dusty earth. Once again, his ability to change direction as he, literally, hared across the ground had saved his life. His brave efforts deserved success.

93

But the second eagle had freed herself from the embarrassment of the bush and was now in the air once more and gaining height, ready for another attack. She soared high on outspread wings, watching the hare's movements, and then closed her wings and dived like an arrow.

Amazingly, the hare managed to reach the shelter of a dense tangle of knobthorn bushes and disappeared underneath as the diving eagle swooped low and missed yet again. She spread her wings wide and flew around the clump of bushes a couple of times, utterly frustrated, before settling in a tree top nearby to keep a close eye on the hare. High above, her mate circled the area watchfully.

Safe for the moment, the hare stayed breathlessly still, his heart beating wildly with fear. He knew nothing about helicopters. His method of survival was to run away – from machines, from man and especially from eagles. He had no way of understanding what happened next.

With a clatter of rotor blades and a great mechanical surge of power, the helicopter prepared to take off. Radio messages had called it away to another part of the Kruger National Park. Dust swirled and leaves flew up in a circle round the rising helicopter. Once again, small animals ran in fright. But the hare was safe outside that wind-blown circle, and hidden for the moment by the wind-blown screen of dust. When

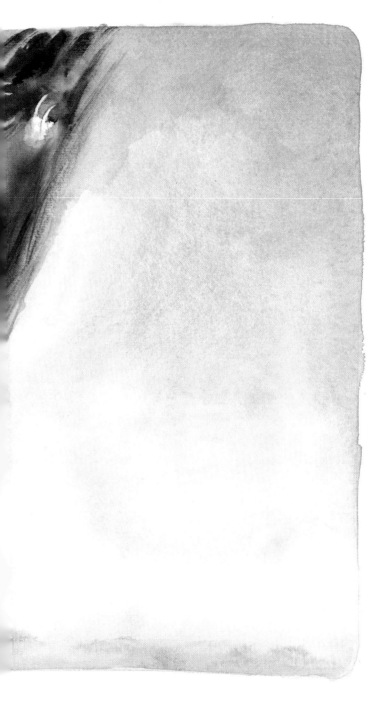

## He that Sweeps Clean

*The first proposal for the preservation of wildlife in the land which was to become the Kruger National Park was agreed on by the Transvaal Volksraad in 1898. After the fighting had ended in the Second Anglo-Boer War, the British reproclaimed the reserve. The Park's first warden was Major James Stevenson-Hamilton whose devotion to the wildlife of South Africa firmly established the Park and ensured its continued expansion. Even those many years ago, the killing of animals by poachers was an enormous problem. Major James Stevenson-Hamilton succeeded in controlling this, and earned his nickname Skukuza (meaning 'he that sweeps clean'). Today, one of the main rest camps is named Skukuza in his honour.*

the helicopter was gone and the local sandstorm had died down, the shelter under the knobthorn bushes was completely empty. The hare had managed to escape – to be hunted, perhaps on yet another day.

The pair of martial eagles soared high, aloof and majestic. Those hunters from the sky were certainly not going to admit that they, like men or hares, could make mistakes.

This happening was spotted by Hugo van Niekerk, and was reported in the pages of *Kiewiet*, the very interesting newsletter of the National Parks Board. We are grateful for permission to retell the story here.

# AUTHOR'S ACKNOWLEDGEMENTS

I would like to extend my warmest thanks to everyone who helped to make these books possible.

## South African Animal Adventures

Roelf Attwell and the Wallers family of Betty's Bay; Walter Mangold; Susan Fowkes;
Nick Carter; Marty Das; Dr EG Nisbet (University of Saskatchewan, Canada); Paul du Toit;
Peter Slingsby; Peter Norton (Department of Nature Conservation, Kimberley);
Joyce Scallan; the Simonstown Naval Museum.

### REFERENCES USED INCLUDE:
*Coelacanth – The fish that came back from the dead* (R Auerbach);
*Dick King, Feats Fame Family* (J Scallan); *Dick King, Saviour of Natal* (C Eyre);
*Discovering Southern Africa* (TV Bulpin); *Huberta the Wandering Hippo* (DA Webb);
*Huberta's Journey* (C van Straten); *Illustrated Guide to Southern Africa* (TV Bulpin);
*Jack the Signalman Baboon* (FW FitzSimons); *Jock of the Bushveld* (P FitzPatrick);
*Just Nuisance, AB* (T Sisson); *Old Fourlegs* (Prof JLB Smith); *The Elephants of Knysna* (N Carter);
*They Came from the Sea* (M Rowe); *They Made This Land* (J Heale); World of Birds newsletters.

## True African Animal Tales

### REFERENCES USED INCLUDE:
*Otter in my parlour* (M Eyre); *Scotty Smith, South Africa's Robin Hood* (FC Metrovich);
*They Made This Land* (J Heale); *The Best of Lawrence Green* (M Barnes);
*Kruger* (Dr Anthony Hall-Martin); *Kiewiet* (National Parks Board).